the
LOSE IT!
magazine
COOKBOOK

the **LOSE IT!** magazine COOKBOOK

CONTENTS

How this works **6**

Five basic rules for eating low carb **8**

What you can and can't eat **10**

In your store cupboard **12**

Vegetarian **17**

Chicken and fish **39**

Meat **83**

Breaking the fast **151**

Nut and dairy free **167**

Sweet treats **183**

Index **205**

HOW THIS WORKS...

Eating low carb is the best thing you can do for your health and wellbeing – it's as simple as that. The reason we know this is because in every issue of our magazine, LOSE IT! – the Low-Carb Way (which launched in April 2014), we share real-life stories of people who have taken the low-carb journey (some of whom you'll meet in this book). Every time these stories come in to the office, the LOSE IT! team clusters around the screen – because the stories are incredible. Not only in terms of the weight loss, which is inspiring enough, but also in terms of reversing (or at the very least, hugely improving) health conditions they believed were there to stay. In nearly all instances where one or more of the following was an issue for them, eating low carb has allowed these people to reverse type 2 diabetes, rid themselves of chronic back pain, vastly improve fibromyalgia, cure chronic fatigue and insomnia, get pregnant… and have access to reserves of energy they never dreamed possible. In a nutshell, over the past two years we've watched hundreds of people get their lives back. More than that – we've watched them fall in love with life again: they love the low-carb recipes, they never feel deprived, they're energetic and positive. They have no trouble keeping the weight off because they can no longer imagine eating any other way.

It is – literally – a life-changing experience. This cookbook is a collection of our best recipes over the past two years, plus 20 brand-new ones (we just can't help ourselves!). They're easy to make but, most importantly, they're all completely satisfying and delicious.

Let the LOSE IT! magazine cookbook change your mind – and your life.

FIVE BASIC RULES FOR EATING LOW CARB

1. Remember LMH: low carb, medium protein, healthy fat.

2. Choose real foods that look like what they are.

3. Fat is not the enemy. Enjoy it!

4. No sugar and no grains.

5. Don't eat if you're not hungry.

Here's to your great good health!

WHAT YOU CAN AND CAN'T EAT

ALWAYS

MEAT
As far as possible, choose grass-fed or organic meats. Enjoy the fat and the skin!

- Bacon (try to find charcuterie bacon, if possible without nitrates and nitrites, and with the lowest carb content – which means the least sugar)
- Beef
- Biltong (for powdered, grind your own)
- Chicken
- Duck
- Game
- Home-cured meats (if buying cured meats, avoid those with sugar and strange chemicals)
- Lamb
- Offal
- Pork
- Sausages containing only meat and spices (no MSG or fillers such as gluten, rusk, soy, sugar and so on)
- Turkey

EGGS
Any way you like, for breakfast, lunch and dinner. Real organic eggs are definitely best, if you can find them.

FRUIT*
- Avocado
- Berries
- Coconut

FISH/ SEAFOOD
(on the SASSI green list, of course!)
The oilier the better.

- Anchovies
- Angelfish
- Calamari (squid)
- Dorado
- Haddock
- Hake
- Kob
- Mackerel
- Mussels
- Prawns
- Salmon
- Sardines
- Scallops
- Snoek
- Trout
- Tuna
- Yellowtail

DRINKS
- All teas (with no milk)
- Coffee (with cream or butter, not milk)
- Sparkling water
- Water

VEGGIES
Rule of thumb here is if it grows above ground, it's generally okay.

- Artichokes
- Asparagus
- Broccoli
- Brussels sprouts
- Cabbage
- Cauliflower
- Celery
- Courgettes (baby marrows or zucchini)
- Cucumber
- Eggplant (aubergine or brinjal)
- Green beans
- Kale
- Lettuce
- Mangetouts (including sugar snap and snow peas)
- Marrows
- Mushrooms
- Olives
- Onions
- Peppers
- Pumpkin
- Radishes
- Spinach
- Tomatoes

SWEET THINGS
- Erythritol
- Stevia
- Xylitol (good quality)

FATS
- Animal fats
- Avocado oil
- Beef and lamb tallow
- Butter
- Coconut cream
- Coconut milk
- Coconut oil
- Dripping
- Duck fat
- Extra virgin olive oil
- Ghee
- Lard
- Macadamia oil
- Mayonnaise (homemade only, using the right oils)

FLOUR
- Almond flour
- Coconut flour
- Hazelnut flour
- Other nut flours

SEEDS
- Chia seeds
- Flaxseeds
- Pumpkin seeds
- Sesame seeds
- Sunflower seeds

NUTS*
- Almonds
- Brazils
- Hazelnuts
- Macadamias
- Pecans
- Pine nuts
- Walnuts

DAIRY*
(all full fat)
While you are trying to lose weight, it may be better to cut out all dairy other than butter. By the way, unsalted butter is delicious in coffee!

- Blue cheeses
- Butter
- Cream (preferably double)
- Cream cheese
- Double cream yoghurt
- Feta cheese
- Ghee
- Parmesan cheese
- All other high-fat cheeses

SOMETIMES

ALCOHOL
- Brandy
- Champagne
- Dry red wine
- Dry white wine
- Rum
- Sparkling wine
- Tequila
- Vodka
- Whisky

SWEET THINGS
- Dark chocolate (80% and above cocoa content – and only very occasionally)
- Honey (no more than 1 tsp at a time, very occasionally – use honey strictly for cooking, otherwise it will seduce you back into sugar cravings in no time!)

NUTS
- Cashews

FRUIT
- All fruit other than berries

VEGGIES
- Beetroot
- Butternut
- Carrots
- Sweet potato

DAIRY
- Milk (only full cream and only very occasionally)

NEVER

ALCOHOL
- Anything labelled 'lite'
- Beer
- Cider
- Cocktails
- Sugary liqueurs

VEGGIES & PULSES
- Beans
- Chickpeas
- Dried beans
- Lentils
- Parsnips
- Peas
- Potatoes

SWEET THINGS
- Agave
- Any artificial sweeteners
- Biscuits
- Cakes
- Chocolate (less than 80% cocoa content)
- Energy drinks
- Fizzy drinks
- Fructose
- Fruit juices
- High-fructose corn syrup
- Ice cream (unless it's LCHF!)
- Malt
- Pastries
- Sugar
- Sweets
- Syrup

MEATS
- Lunch meats
- Processed meats
- Vienna sausages

DRIED FRUIT
- All of it

NUTS
- Peanuts (they're not really nuts)

SOY
- Edamame beans
- Tofu
- All soy – including sausages, etc.

FATS
- Canola oil
- Cottonseed oil
- Flaxseed oil
- Grapeseed oil
- Hemp oil
- Margarine
- Rapeseed oil
- Safflower oil
- Sesame oil
- Soybean oil
- Sunflower oil

GRAINS & CEREALS
- All whole grains
- Amaranth
- Barley
- Bread
- Breakfast cereals
- Bulgur wheat
- Corn
- Couscous
- Crackers
- Millet
- Muesli
- Oats
- Pasta
- Popcorn
- Porridge
- Quinoa
- Rice
- Rye
- Spelt
- Wheat

* If you're eating all the right things and still not losing weight, you may be eating too many nuts, too many berries or too much dairy or protein. Try to cut back and see how it goes.

IN YOUR FRIDGE AND STORE CUPBOARD

OILS, SAUCES AND VINEGARS

- Apple cider vinegar
- Balsamic vinegar
- Coconut oil
- Extra virgin olive oil
- Fish sauce
- Macadamia oil
- Mayonnaise (homemade)
- Red wine vinegar
- White wine vinegar

BASIC INGREDIENTS

- 80% or darker chocolate
- Almond flour
- Almond nut butter
- Almonds
- Baking powder
- Black olives
- Canned artichokes
- Canned cherry tomatoes
- Canned chopped tomatoes
- Canned italian tomatoes
- Caper berries
- Capers
- Cocoa powder
- Coconut cream
- Coconut flour
- Coconut milk
- Desiccated coconut
- Dijon mustard
- Gelatine
- Goji berries
- Green olives
- Harissa paste
- Honey
- Macadamia nuts
- Orange blossom water
- Passata (homemade)
- Pine nuts
- Pistachio nuts
- Poppy seeds
- Psyllium husks
- Pumpkin seeds
- Red wine (dry)
- Rosewater
- Sesame seeds
- Tahini
- Thai red curry paste
- Tomato paste
- Vanilla extract
- Walnuts
- White wine (dry)
- Wholegrain mustard
- Xylitol

DRIED SPICES AND HERBS

- Allspice
- Black pepper
- Cardamom pods
- Cayenne pepper
- Celery salt
- Cinnamon sticks
- Cloves
- Coarse salt
- Coriander seeds
- Cumin seeds
- Curry powder
- Dried chilli flakes
- Dried curry leaves
- Dried italian herbs
- Dried oregano
- Dried rosemary
- Dried thyme
- Fennel seeds
- Fenugreek leaves
- Garam masala
- Ground cinnamon
- Ground coriander
- Ground cumin
- Ground ginger
- Ground nutmeg
- Himalayan salt
- Mustard powder
- Mustard seeds
- Paprika
- Pink peppercorns
- Saffron
- Smoked paprika
- Star anise
- Turmeric
- Vanilla pods

ALTERNATIVES TO GRAINS

Because grains are not allowed as part of a low-carb diet, we have devised some delicious alternatives.

Cauli 'pizza' is a yummy low-carb alternative to a regular dough base that is made with wheat flour. The recipe for a cauliflower base is given on page 73. If you don't have the time to make your own low-carb cauliflower bases, use ready-made low-carb cauliflower or pumpkin wraps, which are available at many health stores and selected large supermarkets.

Cauliflower 'rice' is made by pulsing raw cauliflower florets in a food processor until fine in texture. This can then be steamed or blanched for 1–2 minutes before serving. For convenience, some large supermarkets stock ready-prepared cauliflower 'rice' in their fruit and vegetable section. **Broccoli 'rice'** can be similarly prepared and should be steamed or blanched for 2 minutes.

Cauliflower 'mash' or **pumpkin 'mash'** is made by puréeing soft, boiled and drained cauliflower florets or peeled pumpkin chunks to form a smooth 'mash', which can be seasoned with salt and pepper and served in place of mashed potatoes.

Courgette 'noodles', or **'zoodles'**, are whole courgettes that have been spiralised to form long, noodle-like strands. These can be steamed or blanched for ½ minute before serving. Spiralisers are available from most kitchen stores. For convenience, some large supermarkets stock ready-prepared courgette 'noodles' in their fruit and vegetable section.

Vegetarian

JUSTINE
KIGGEN

LOSE IT! food editor

When I started working on LOSE IT! I was a mainstream food editor, writing conventional recipes and styling as I had done for the last 10 years or so. I was a little apprehensive at first about LCHF (low carb, healthy fat), but once I started writing recipes and learning to understand the low-carb way, I began to realise how beneficial this way of eating could be to many people, including myself. As I learned more about this new way of cooking and eating, I also adapted my lifestyle at home – not only in my work kitchen. For some people over the age of 40, the possibility of insulin resistance and diabetes is a growing reality and one I, too, don't want to face in the future. I'm now studying nutrition to gain an in-depth understanding of the science behind it all: I believe that it is possible to heal and manage most of the lifestyle conditions we struggle with in modern times through our nutritional choices. Most people only make changes when they get sick and I believe that prevention through nutrition goes a long way. I wish I had learnt about the low-carb lifestyle sooner. It has changed both the way I cook and the ingredients I use. One of the things I've rediscovered is salad! I think it's totally underrated, especially in South Africa. My meals now always include a hearty salad. I feel healthier, more energised and I want to share the knowledge and delicious recipes with the world.

Cauli pizza with tomato, blue cheese and walnut topping

Serves 4

KEEP ON TRACK *per serving*

Fat 42g | Carbs 18g | Protein 36g

4 store-bought or readymade cauli pizza bases

FOR THE TOPPING
300g baby tomatoes, halved
100g blue cheese, crumbled
100g mozzarella, torn
100g walnuts, toasted

extra virgin olive oil, for drizzling
wild rocket, to serve

1. Preheat the oven to 200°C.
2. Place the pizza bases on a baking tray, divide tomatoes
and cheeses between the bases and sprinkle walnuts on top.
Bake in the oven for 15 minutes.
3. To serve: Drizzle with a little olive oil and top with
wild rocket.

Baked mushrooms and goat's cheese

Serves 4

KEEP ON TRACK *per serving*

Fat 57g | Carbs 12g | Protein 23g

FOR THE MUSHROOMS
800g medium brown mushrooms
extra virgin olive oil, for drizzling
himalayan salt and black pepper
100g goat's cheese, crumbled
fresh thyme

FOR THE DRESSING
2 tsp red wine vinegar
2 garlic cloves, finely minced
⅓ cup extra virgin olive oil

TO SERVE
200g wild rocket
300g bacon rashers, finely sliced into batons and fried
50g walnuts, toasted and roughly chopped

1. For the mushrooms: Preheat the oven to 200°C. Place the mushrooms on a baking tray, drizzle with olive oil and season, top with cheese and fresh thyme and bake for 7–10 minutes.
2. For the dressing: In a small jug, whisk together the red wine vinegar and garlic. Slowly add olive oil and whisk to combine. Season.
3. To serve: Place the mushrooms on a plate, sprinkle the rocket, bacon and walnuts over the top and drizzle with dressing.

Moutabel-style eggplant dip

Serves 4–6

KEEP ON TRACK *per serving*

Fat 20g | Carbs 11g | Protein 6g

2 large eggplants
1 garlic clove, crushed
1 tsp each cumin seeds, paprika and ground coriander, toasted
2g fresh basil
2g fresh mint
1 green chilli, chopped
3 tbsp tahini
3 tbsp extra virgin olive oil
juice of ½ lemon
½ cup double cream yoghurt
himalayan salt and black pepper

pomegranate rubies, to serve

1. Preheat the oven to 180°C. Place the eggplants on an oven tray, prick all over and roast until soft, about 30–40 minutes. Remove from the oven and allow to cool.
2. Halve the eggplants, remove the flesh, place in a sieve over a bowl and press out as much liquid as possible. Then spoon the flesh into a food processor with remaining ingredients and blitz until fairly smooth.
3. To serve: Top with pomegranate rubies and serve with fresh dipping vegetables such as radishes, spring onions and cucumber.

Broccoli and cauliflower falafels

Serves 4–6

KEEP ON TRACK *per serving*

Fat 34g | Carbs 18g | Protein 12g

FOR THE FALAFELS
100g broccoli 'rice'
280g cauli 'rice'
1 small red onion, sliced
2 garlic cloves, chopped
130g walnuts, toasted and chopped
2 tsp ground cumin
7g fresh parsley, chopped
5g fresh mint, chopped
1 large egg
2 tsp baking powder
himalayan salt and black pepper

coconut oil, for deep-frying

FOR THE SAUCE
2 tsp lemon juice
1 cup double cream yoghurt
5g each fresh mint and dill, finely chopped
paprika, to sprinkle

sesame seeds, to scatter

1. For the falafels: Heat a pan over medium heat, add the broccoli and cauli 'rice' and cook for 3–4 minutes to remove all excess moisture, then set aside and allow to cool. Place in a food processor, add remaining falafel ingredients and blitz to combine. Then form into small balls.
2. Heat the oil to 180°C, fry the balls until golden and crispy, then drain on paper towel.
3. For the sauce: Whisk the lemon juice, yoghurt and herbs together and sprinkle paprika on top.
4. To serve: Serve falafels hot, with sesame seeds scattered over the top, and with dipping sauce on the side.

Spicy cauliflower salad with poached egg

Serves 4

per serving

Fat 17g | Carbs 14g | Protein 13g

1 tbsp ghee
1 garlic clove, crushed
3cm piece ginger, finely grated
1 tbsp mustard seeds
1 tbsp garam masala
1 tsp turmeric
1 tsp cumin seeds
500g cauliflower florets
1 cup homemade vegetable stock
himalayan salt and black pepper

TO SERVE
2 tomatoes, diced
4 eggs, poached
3 tbsp flaked almonds, toasted
fresh coriander

1. Heat ghee in a pot and fry garlic, ginger and spices for 3 minutes.
2. Add the cauliflower and stock and cook for 15 minutes, or until tender and stock is reduced. Season to taste.
3. To serve: Divide cauliflower between 4 serving plates, top with tomato, poached egg, almonds and fresh coriander.

Mini eggplant pizzas

Serves 4

per serving

Fat 9g | Carbs 14g | Protein 13g

2 large eggplants, thickly sliced into rounds
coarse salt, for sprinkling

FOR THE TOPPING
150g mozzarella cheese, grated
100g rosa tomatoes, halved
8 anchovy fillets, halved
1 tsp dried oregano
himalayan salt and black pepper

fresh basil leaves, to serve

1. Place the eggplant rounds on a surface, sprinkle with coarse salt
and leave for 30 minutes. Remove the salt and dab off any moisture.
2. Preheat the oven to 200°C. Place the eggplant rounds on a baking
tray and cook for 20 minutes, or until slightly softened (but not too soft).
Remove from the oven and allow to cool slightly.
3. For the topping: Top each round with a sprinkling of mozzarella,
some rosa tomato halves and anchovy fillet, and a little oregano.
Season to taste.
4. Return to the oven and cook for 7–10 minutes, or until cheese
has melted and turned golden.
5. To serve: Serve hot topped with fresh basil leaves.

Anchovy and courgette fritters with basil cream sauce

Serves 4–6

KEEP ON TRACK *per serving*
Fat 46g | Carbs 14g | Protein 11g

FOR THE FRITTERS
700g courgettes, grated
7 anchovy fillets, mashed
5g fresh parsley, finely chopped
2 eggs, beaten
3 tbsp coconut flour
2 tsp baking powder
himalayan salt and black pepper

coconut oil, for frying

FOR THE CREAM SAUCE
1½ cups cream
1 garlic clove, minced
5g fresh basil, finely chopped

chopped red onion, to garnish
lemon wedges, to serve

1. For the fritters: Place the grated courgettes in a clean dish towel and squeeze out as much moisture as possible, then place in a bowl with the remaining ingredients and stir well.
2. Heat the oil in a pan and fry dollops of the mixture on both sides until browned, then drain on paper towel.
3. For the sauce: Place the cream in a small pot, add the garlic and basil, bring to a boil, then simmer for 5 minutes until thickened, and season to taste.
4. To serve: Serve fritters hot, garnished with chopped red onion, with cream sauce and lemon wedges on the side.

Winter vegetable bake

Serves 4

KEEP ON TRACK *per serving*

Fat 18g | Carbs 25g | Protein 17g

2 tbsp coconut oil, melted
4 eggs, beaten
100g double cream yoghurt
10g chives, chopped
himalayan salt and black pepper
5 large green courgettes, sliced
4 yellow marrows, sliced
3 large tomatoes, sliced
2 small eggplants, sliced
3 garlic cloves, finely chopped
50g parmesan, grated
fresh basil, to serve

1. Preheat the oven to 160°C. Brush a 22cm round oven dish with the coconut oil.
2. Whisk together eggs, yoghurt and chives, and season.
3. Arrange vegetable slices in the dish, alternating the vegetables in a spiral, and sprinkling garlic in between.
4. Pour the egg mixture over the top and sprinkle with grated parmesan.
5. Bake for 30–40 minutes, or until golden and cooked through.
6. To serve: Serve hot, topped with fresh basil.

Chicken

and

fish

CHICKEN

HENNIE COETZEE

Foodie and wine connoisseur

'After seeing a photo of myself on holiday I thought, "I've got to do something – I can't go through life looking like this." I'd followed a different diet and lost weight previously but it was so strict and required seriously rigorous exercise. I was about to start on that again when I heard about banting. I read the science and it made sense to me so I tried it. You won't believe how quickly I lost weight – it was 10 to 12kg a month for the first couple of months without giving up wine! When I started I was so heavy that I didn't register on the scale – I was probably about 200kg. The first two weeks were extremely tough as I had no energy – my body was in complete shock. The moment your body switches over and you go into ketosis for the first time ever, it's unbelievable how good you feel. You suddenly have all this energy – I felt like running! I've lost 107kg without ever feeling hungry, my concentration and focus have gone through the roof, I can go out and find clothes that actually fit and I'm more active than I've ever been. I run on average 200km a month, do yoga three times a week and I still drink tons of wine! It's been unbelievable – absolutely life-changing in every way.'

http://batonage.com

Hennie's coconut chicken curry

Serves 4

Fat 64g | Carbs 31g | Protein 34g

FOR THE PASTE
1 tbsp coconut oil
1 onion, sliced
75g cashews, toasted
½ cup coconut cream
¼ cup double cream yoghurt
himalayan salt and black pepper

FOR THE CURRY
2 tbsp coconut oil
1 onion, diced
1½ tbsp minced garlic
1½ tbsp minced ginger
1 × 410g can diced tomatoes
1 tbsp ground coriander
1 tbsp red chilli powder
1 dried red chilli, chopped
1 tsp turmeric
1 tbsp chopped fenugreek leaves
5 curry leaves
100g ghee
4 chicken breast fillets, cut into cubes
2 tbsp garam masala

1. For the paste: Heat a pan, add coconut oil and sauté the onion until golden brown. Remove, allow to cool, place in a food processer with the toasted cashew nuts and process until the mixture forms a smooth paste. Add the coconut cream and yoghurt and process again until combined. Season and set aside.

2. For the curry: Heat coconut oil in a pot, toss in the onion, garlic and ginger and cook until softened and golden. Pour in the tomatoes and stir to combine. Cook for 2 minutes then add the spices and leaves and sauté for an additional minute. Reduce the heat to low, add the ghee, and allow to cook for 15–20 minutes. Toss in the chicken and simmer until cooked through. Add garam masala and paste, stir and cook gently for 3–4 minutes, or until heated through.

3. To serve: Serve curry with cauli 'rice', fresh coriander and sliced red onion and chilli.

Spatchcock chicken with lemon peri-peri butter

Serves 6

KEEP ON TRACK *per serving*

Fat 80g | Carbs 5g | Protein 101g

2 spatchcock chickens
2 cups buttermilk

FOR THE PERI-PERI BUTTER
130g butter, softened
1 tsp dried chilli flakes, crushed
2 garlic cloves, chopped
2 spring onions or salad onions, finely chopped
grated zest and juice of 1 lemon
himalayan salt and black pepper

FOR THE BASTING SAUCE
3 tbsp coconut oil, melted
2 tsp white wine vinegar
1½ tsp paprika
pinch of cayenne pepper
big pinch dried chilli flakes

fresh lemons, to serve
homemade peri-peri sauce, to serve

1. Place the chickens in a shallow dish, pour buttermilk over them and allow to stand for 30 minutes. Then drain and scrape off most of the buttermilk.
2. For the butter: Mix all the butter ingredients together, then push the butter under the skin of the chicken as far back as it will go and season the chicken well.
3. For the basting sauce: Mix all the basting sauce ingredients together and brush over the chicken.
4. Place the chicken over the braai and cover with foil or a lid. Cook for 30–40 minutes, or until golden and cooked through, basting occasionally.
5. To serve: Cut into portions and serve with extra lemon segments, chargrilled over the braai, and peri-peri sauce.

Chicken salad with mint dressing

Serves 4

KEEP ON TRACK *per serving*

Fat 18g | Carbs 25g | Protein 30g

FOR THE CHICKEN
1 tsp curry powder
1 tsp turmeric
5cm piece ginger, cut into strips
1 tbsp mustard seeds, crushed
grated zest and juice of 1 lemon
2 garlic cloves, crushed
1–2 tbsp extra virgin olive oil
4 chicken breast fillets, flattened

FOR THE DRESSING
½ tsp cumin seeds
½ tsp whole coriander seeds
1 tsp fennel seeds
1 cup double cream yoghurt
10g mint, chopped
½ cucumber, peeled, seeded and chopped
squeeze of fresh lemon juice

FOR THE SALAD
3 large carrots, cut into strips
2 baby fennel bulbs, sliced
150g mixed salad leaves
½ red onion, chopped
75g pomegranate rubies

1. For the chicken: Place the curry powder, turmeric, ginger, mustard seeds, lemon juice and zest, garlic and oil in a small bowl and stir well to combine. Rub mixture onto chicken breasts.
2. Heat a griddle pan, cook chicken well, remove and set aside to cool.
3. For the dressing: Pound the seeds and whisk together with the other ingredients.
4. For the salad: Place carrot, fennel, salad leaves, red onion and pomegranate rubies in a bowl and toss together.
5. To serve: Divide salad between 4 plates. Top with sliced chicken and serve dressing on the side.

Paprika chicken with a buttermilk chive dressing and pumpkin chunks

Serves 4

KEEP ON TRACK *per serving*

Fat 51g | Carbs 14g | Protein 48g

FOR THE MARINADE
1 tsp smoked paprika
⅓ cup dry white wine
2 garlic cloves, crushed
1 tbsp fresh oregano
¼ cup extra virgin olive oil
himalayan salt and black pepper, to taste

8 chicken drumsticks and thighs, skin on
100g green olives, drained

FOR THE SAUCE
½ cup buttermilk
juice of 1 lemon
2 tsp xylitol
10g chives, chopped
himalayan salt and black pepper

500g diced pumpkin, roasted

1. Preheat the oven to 200°C.
2. For the marinade: In a large shallow bowl whisk all the marinade ingredients together. Add the chicken and stir well to coat. Allow to stand for 10 minutes.
3. Place in a roasting dish, scatter the olives over the top and roast for 25 minutes or until cooked through. Remove from the oven and set aside.
4. For the sauce: Whisk all the ingredients together and season well.
5. To serve: Serve chicken hot with buttermilk sauce and roasted pumpkin chunks.

Rolled stuffed chicken breasts

Serves 4

KEEP ON TRACK *per serving*

Fat 27g | Carbs 11g | Protein 46g

FOR THE FILLING
2 tsp coconut oil
1 onion, finely chopped
2 garlic cloves, crushed
1 tsp dried chilli flakes
2 cups finely chopped broccoli
50g pine nuts, toasted
3 tbsp chopped fresh oregano
himalayan salt and black pepper

4 large chicken breasts, deboned, skin on
80g thinly sliced gruyère cheese
1 tbsp ghee

mixed herb salad and red pepper pesto, to serve

1. For the filling: Heat the coconut oil in a frying pan. Fry the onion until golden, add the garlic, chilli flakes and broccoli and cook for 5 minutes or until tender. Stir in pine nuts and oregano and season to taste. Set aside.
2. Heat oven to 180°C. Using a mallet or rolling pin, carefully flatten the chicken breasts skin-side down until they are an even thickness.
3. Arrange slices of gruyère on chicken breasts, top with the filling and roll each breast into a cylinder. Wrap each cylinder tightly in foil and roast for 30–40 minutes, or until cooked through. When done, unwrap the chicken rolls and fry in the ghee until browned.
4. To serve: Slice chicken rolls and serve with salad and red pepper pesto.

Spicy coconut chicken curry

Serves 4

KEEP ON TRACK *per serving*

Fat 47g | Carbs 33g | Protein 61g

½ cup double cream yoghurt
2 garlic cloves, crushed
juice of 1 lime
pinch of saffron in a little hot water
1 tbsp each ground cumin and coriander
½ tsp paprika
1kg boneless chicken thighs
1 tbsp ghee

FOR THE CURRY
2 tbsp ghee
1 onion, chopped
10g fresh ginger, chopped
1 red or green chilli, chopped
1 tsp each turmeric and garam masala
1 × 410g can crushed tomatoes
100g ground almonds, toasted
1 × 400g can coconut cream

TO SERVE
cauli 'rice'
fresh coriander
chopped onion and tomato

1. Place the yoghurt, garlic, lime juice and spices in a bowl, add the chicken, cover and refrigerate for 1 hour. Then scrape off the marinade and reserve it.
2. Heat 1 tbsp ghee in a large pan, brown the chicken on all sides, remove and set aside.
3. For the curry: Heat the ghee in the pan, add the onion, ginger, chilli and spices and sauté until golden. Add the remaining ingredients, plus the chicken and reserved marinade, bring to a simmer and cook for 30 minutes or until thickened.
4. To serve: Serve with cauli 'rice' and fresh coriander, with chopped onion and tomato on the side.

Yoghurt-marinated chicken with coriander sauce

Serves 4

KEEP ON TRACK *per serving*

Fat 73g | Carbs 11g | Protein 74g

FOR THE MARINADE
1 cup double cream yoghurt
2 tsp paprika
1 tsp turmeric
2 tsp garam masala
juice of 1 lemon
2 tbsp ghee, melted
himalayan salt and black pepper

3 stalks celery
1 red onion, cut into wedges
1 whole chicken

FOR THE SAUCE
30g coriander, leaves and stems
½ cup double cream yoghurt
½ cup desiccated coconut
squeeze of fresh lemon juice

1. For the marinade: Mix all the marinade ingredients together and season to taste.
2. Arrange celery and onion in a roasting dish and top with the chicken, cover the chicken with the marinade and allow to stand for 30–60 minutes.
3. Preheat the oven to 180°C. Roast the chicken for 1 hour 15 minutes or until cooked through. Remove and set aside.
4. For the sauce: Place all the ingredients in a blender and blitz until smooth.
5. To serve: Carve the chicken into portions and top with the sauce.

Grilled chicken and rocket pesto with zoodles

Serves 4

KEEP ON TRACK *per serving*

Fat 41g | Carbs 6g | Protein 32g

FOR THE PESTO
1 garlic clove, chopped
50g flaked almonds, toasted
80g wild rocket
50g pecorino cheese, grated
⅓ cup extra virgin olive oil
himalayan salt and black pepper

FOR THE CHICKEN
½ tsp smoked paprika
2 tsp salt
1 tsp ground cumin
2 tbsp coconut oil, melted
4 chicken breast fillets

500g zoodles (courgette 'noodles'), blanched
grated parmesan cheese, to serve

1. For the pesto: Blitz the garlic and almonds in a food processor to combine.
Add the rocket and pecorino, blitz again, then slowly add the oil until combined.
Season and set aside.
2. For the chicken: In a small bowl, mix together the paprika, salt and cumin, add
the coconut oil and stir to combine. Brush the mixture onto the chicken fillets.
3. Heat a griddle pan and cook the chicken on both sides for 4–5 minutes,
or until cooked through.
4. To serve: Thickly slice the chicken fillets, place on a bed of zoodles and top
with dollops of pesto and a sprinkling of parmesan.

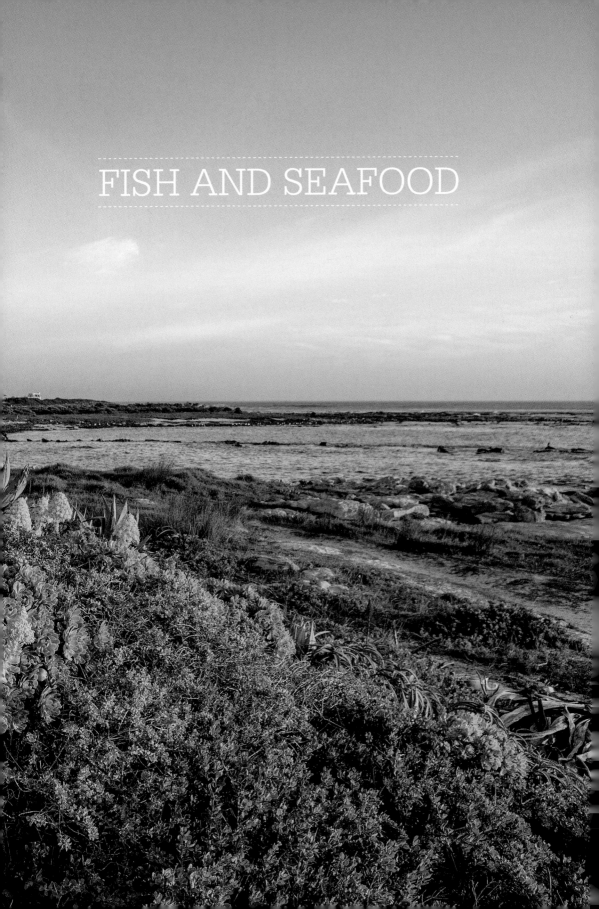

FISH AND SEAFOOD

NICKY PERKS

Banting Buddies founder

'For as long as I can remember, I have been trying to lose weight. Even though I was very sporty as a child, I was chubby. In my late twenties I got very into running and hoped that the extra exercise would help me lose weight. I trained for half marathons, ran them, and yet didn't lose a single kilogram! The more I ran, the hungrier I got. After two pregnancies, I was 30kg overweight, and desperate. I looked and felt awful. I had no energy and struggled to get through the day with two small children. I knew I had to find a solution, to be the mom and wife I wanted to be. My low-carb journey really started when I read *The Primal Blueprint* by Mark Sisson and *The Art and Science of Low Carbohydrate Living* by Steve Phinney and Jeff Volek. Because I have polycystic ovary syndrome (PCOS) and as a result am insulin resistant, my weight loss was slow but steady. My energy levels, skin and mood all improved, plus my chronic hay fever disappeared. I've lost 16kg so far and I've finally been liberated from my intense sugar cravings. The great thing about the low-carb lifestyle is the food is delicious, I don't feel hungry or deprived, and I have never felt healthier or more energetic. My husband and kids are also loving it and reaping the health benefits.'

https://primalperks.com

Nicky's garlic, ginger and coconut prawns

Serves 4

KEEP ON TRACK *per serving*

Fat 27g | Carbs 8g | Protein 34g

2 tbsp coconut oil
1 tbsp crushed garlic
1 tbsp finely chopped fresh ginger
1–2 fresh red chillies, chopped
1 tsp turmeric
600g medium-sized prawns (deveined, in shell, with heads on)
1 × 165ml can coconut cream
himalayan salt and black pepper

TO SERVE
butter-braised cabbage or cauli 'rice'
10g fresh coriander, chopped
12 rosa tomatoes, sliced
3 red spring onions, chopped

1. Melt coconut oil in a wok, toss in the garlic, ginger, chilli and turmeric and sauté for 1 minute.
2. Add prawns to wok and cook for another minute.
3. Pour in coconut cream and simmer until prawns are cooked through and pink. Season to taste.
4. To serve: Serve on a bed of butter-braised cabbage or cauli 'rice' and top with coriander, tomato and spring onion.

Note: More coconut milk can be added if more sauce is desired.

Snoek with fresh tomato salad and watercress pesto

Serves 4

Fat 52g | Carbs 16g | Protein 51g

FOR THE FISH
800g side lightly smoked snoek
2 tbsp butter
grated zest and juice of 1 lemon
10g flat-leaf parsley, chopped
1 garlic clove, crushed
himalayan salt and black pepper

FOR THE PESTO
60g watercress
30g fresh basil
2 garlic cloves
50g blanched almonds
50g parmesan cheese, grated
½ cup extra virgin olive oil

TO SERVE
400g exotic tomato selection, sliced or halved if small
2 ripe red tomatoes, sliced
watercress

1. Preheat the oven to 180°C.
2. For the fish: Place the fish skin-side down on a lightly greased sheet of foil.
3. Combine butter, lemon zest and juice, parsley and garlic, and rub over the fish. Season and cover the fish with another sheet of foil. Cook in the oven for 15–20 minutes, and then set aside.
4. For the pesto: Place all the pesto ingredients in a blender and blitz until smooth. Season to taste.
5. To serve: Arrange the fish and tomatoes on a platter, garnish with watercress and drizzle pesto over the top.

Crumbed hake and courgette fries

Serves 4

KEEP ON TRACK *per serving*

Fat 44g | Carbs 18g | Protein 50g

800g hake fillet
himalayan salt and black pepper
2 eggs, whisked
100g desiccated coconut
5g flat-leaf parsley, chopped
3 tbsp coconut oil, for frying

FOR THE COURGETTE FRIES
2 egg whites
50g parmesan cheese, grated
himalayan salt and black pepper
8 courgettes, cut into strips
3 tbsp duck fat, for frying

TO SERVE
creamed horseradish
lemon wedges
fresh thyme

1. Cut the hake into chunks and season well. Place the eggs in a shallow container and mix the coconut and parsley in a second container. Dunk the fish first into the beaten egg, then into the coconut and parsley, and set aside.
2. Heat the coconut oil in a pan and cook the fish on both sides until golden and cooked through. Remove and drain on paper towel.
3. For the courgette fries: Whisk the egg whites lightly, place the parmesan in a bowl and season well. Dip the courgette strips in the egg white and then toss to coat in the seasoned parmesan; repeat until all the courgette strips are coated.
4. Heat the duck fat, add the courgettes in batches and fry until crispy and golden.
5. To serve: Serve the fish with the courgette fries, creamed horseradish and lemon wedges, and garnish with herbs.

Asian-style salmon and cucumber salad

Serves 4

KEEP ON TRACK *per serving*

Fat 41g | Carbs 4g | Protein 37g

600g salmon or trout fillets, skin on
coconut oil, for brushing
himalayan salt and black pepper

FOR THE SALAD
1 cucumber, finely sliced
½ cup finely sliced radish
2g fresh mint
2g fresh basil
2g fresh coriander
2 spring onions, finely sliced

FOR THE DRESSING
2 tbsp large salted capers, rinsed
grated zest of 1 lime
3½ tbsp macadamia oil

4 eggs, poached

1. Preheat the oven to 180°C. Brush fish with coconut oil, place on
a baking tray and bake for 15–20 minutes. Remove and set aside to cool.
2. For the salad: Toss together the salad ingredients.
3. For the dressing: Place the capers, lime zest and macadamia oil in a
small bowl, stir to combine.
4. To serve: Place the salad ingredients on a platter, top with the
fish and poached eggs, and drizzle with the dressing.

Deluxe cauli pizza with crème fraîche and smoked salmon

Serves 4

Fat 32g | Carbs 11g | Protein 25g

FOR THE BASE
500g cauliflower, finely chopped or processed
110g mozzarella cheese, grated
25g parmesan cheese, grated
1 large egg, beaten
1 tsp each dried oregano, rosemary and thyme

FOR THE TOPPING
230g crème fraîche
100g smoked salmon or smoked salmon trout, sliced
8 caper berries
¼ red onion, finely sliced
1 tbsp black or red lumpfish roe (optional)

100g micro green salad, to garnish

1. For the base: Preheat the oven to 180°C.
2. Combine all the base ingredients in a large bowl until well mixed.
3. Place mixture on a greased, foil-lined baking tray and press it out into an even rectangle shape. Bake for 25 minutes, or until golden brown and firm to the touch.
4. Allow to cool slightly and carefully transfer base to a serving plate.
5. For the topping: Spread the crème fraîche over the pizza base and arrange the salmon over it. Top with caper berries, onion slices and fish roe.
6. To serve: Serve immediately with a scattering of micro greens.

Smoked salmon and cream cheese terrine

Serves 6

KEEP ON TRACK *per serving*

Fat 36g | Carbs 7g | Protein 22g

500g smoked salmon, or smoked trout ribbons
1 cucumber, finely sliced into ribbons
500g full fat cream cheese, at room temperature
½ cup cream
10g chives, finely chopped
grated zest and juice of 1 lemon
2 tsp pink peppercorns, roughly crushed
himalayan salt and white pepper

lemon slices and fresh coriander, to serve

1. Lightly oil a 1ℓ capacity loaf tin, then line it with enough muslin so that the muslin hangs well over the edges. Layer smoked salmon on the base and sides of the tin so that the whole tin is covered.
2. Salt the cucumber ribbons and place in a strainer. Set aside for 30 minutes. Rinse and dry very well.
3. Place the cream cheese in a bowl, add the cream and whisk until smooth and thick. Stir in the chives, lemon zest and juice and pink peppercorns. Season well.
4. Place ⅓ of the mixture in the base of the salmon-lined tin, top with a layer of cucumber, then a layer of salmon, and repeat these steps so that you have 3 layers.
5. Fold the muslin over the final layer of salmon. Refrigerate overnight.
6. To serve: Invert the loaf tin onto a serving plate and gently remove the loaf tin and muslin. Slice the terrine and serve with lemon slices and fresh coriander.

Catalan tomato fish with saffron and mayonnaise

Serves 4

KEEP ON TRACK *per serving*

Fat 52g | Carbs 11g | Protein 40g

100g chorizo, sliced
30g dried olives
2 garlic cloves, minced
1 tsp allspice
2 bay leaves
½ cup dry white wine
pinch of saffron threads
2 cups homemade passata
1 cup homemade fish stock
1 preserved lemon wedge, chopped
700g hake fillets, cut into chunks
5g fresh parsley, chopped
himalayan salt and black pepper

FOR THE MAYONNAISE
2 egg yolks
1 tsp dijon mustard
1 garlic clove, minced
¾ cup macadamia oil
juice of a small lemon
himalayan salt and black pepper

1. Heat a large pot, add the chorizo, olives and garlic; pan-fry until golden, then add the allspice, bay leaves, wine and saffron. Bring to a boil, then reduce heat and simmer for 5 minutes.
2. Add the passata, fish stock and lemon. Simmer for an additional 5 minutes, then gently add the fish, turn the heat down very low and cook for 2–3 minutes. Switch off the heat, stir in the parsley and allow the pot to stand, covered, for 5 minutes. Season well.
3. For the mayonnaise: Whisk the egg yolks, mustard and garlic until pale, then slowly whisk in the oil until the mixture thickens. Stir in the lemon juice and season to taste.
4. To serve: Serve fish hot, with mayonnaise.

Cumin-roasted cauliflower with prawns

Serves 4

KEEP ON TRACK *per serving*

Fat 38g | Carbs 21g | Protein 22g

1½ large heads cauliflower, broken into small florets
2 tsp cumin seeds
1 tsp coriander seeds
½ tsp dried chilli flakes
2 tbsp coconut oil, melted
himalayan salt and black pepper

FOR THE PRAWNS
2 tbsp ghee
2 garlic cloves, chopped
1 red or green chilli, finely chopped
400g whole prawns, heads removed

FOR THE DRESSING
½ cup homemade mayonnaise (see page 76)
½ cup buttermilk
juice of 1 lime
2 tsp xylitol
5g fresh coriander, chopped

baby radishes, to garnish

1. Preheat the oven to 200°C. Place the florets on a roasting tray, sprinkle with spices, drizzle with coconut oil and season to taste. Roast until crispy and golden brown, about 30 minutes, then remove from the oven and allow to cool slightly.
2. For the prawns: Heat the ghee, garlic and chilli in a pan, toss in the prawns and sauté until pink and cooked through. Season well.
3. For the dressing: Whisk together all the ingredients, then season.
4. To serve: Place the roasted cauliflower on a platter, top with the prawn mixture and serve warm, drizzled with dressing, with baby radishes on the side.

Tomato prawn salad with herbed feta and tomato dressing

Serves 4

KEEP ON TRACK *per serving*

Fat 32g | Carbs 15g | Protein 30g

FOR THE SALAD
3 large tomatoes, cut into slices
2 avocados, peeled, cut into wedges
½ red onion, finely sliced
100g feta, crumbled
24 prawns, peeled and cooked
himalayan salt and black pepper

FOR THE DRESSING
150g mixed cherry tomatoes, chopped
1 tsp xylitol
10g chives, chopped
1 tsp apple cider vinegar
¼ cup macadamia oil

1. For the salad: Arrange the salad ingredients on 4 serving plates and season to taste.
2. For the dressing: In a small bowl, stir together the tomato, xylitol, chives and vinegar. Then gently whisk in the oil and season to taste.
3. To serve: Pour the dressing over the salad and serve.

Meat

BEEF, LAMB AND PORK

BEEF

BRIAN BERKMAN

Public relations consultant

'I'd had issues with food since childhood. And the fact that I became a public relations foodie and restaurant critic as an adult didn't help. In July 2011, I weighed 153kg. My health was compromised: I had chronic back pain, type 2 diabetes and high blood pressure. When my doctor said bariatric surgery was my only solution, I decided to go through with it. It was just lucky that two postponements gave me time to shed weight by following a strict low-calorie, low-carb diet. I cut out dairy and sugar immediately and lost 25kg in three months. I decided to continue without the surgery, and knew I would have to change my life as well as my diet.

'So I stopped writing about food, and shifted my focus to travel. And, crucially, I decided to follow Prof. Tim Noakes's advice rather than my dietician's: he advised cutting carbs and increasing fat. When I did that, my weight loss accelerated and I had no more cravings. It was a real revelation.

I've lost over 70kg in total and have been at my ideal body weight for over three years. I follow a LCHF diet, and I will never eat any other way. I no longer need medication for diabetes – which is extraordinary, given that I was previously on the maximum oral dose. Every time I hear detractors, I feel even more committed to this lifestyle. I have been given a second chance in life and cannot tell you how much I'm loving it!'

http://brianberkman.com

BRIAN
BERKMAN
(LEFT) WITH
HIS SPOUSE
JEAN-PIERRE
FLUCKIGER.

Brian's brisket

Serves 8

KEEP ON TRACK *per serving*

Fat 58g | Carbs 17g | Protein 50g

2kg beef brisket, deboned
2 × 70g packets of thai red curry paste
2 × 410g cans diced tomatoes
2 × 400g cans coconut milk
1 tbsp himalayan salt

grated zest and juice of 2 limes or 1 lemon
cauli 'rice' or store-bought cauli wraps

1. Dry the meat with paper towel and spread the curry paste over both sides.
2. Preheat the oven to 110°C. Place the brisket in a large ovenproof pot or dish, with a lid, add all the canned tomatoes, one can coconut milk and the salt, cover and cook for 6 hours, or until the meat is soft enough to pull apart with forks.
3. After cooking, remove the meat from the sauce, reserving the sauce, and shred the meat using two forks. Season to taste. If desired, a second can of coconut milk can be added to the sauce at this point and mixed in using an immersion blender.
4. Preheat the oven to 180°C. Return the shredded meat to the sauce, and cook the brisket and sauce for another hour.
5. To serve: Add the grated lime or lemon zest and juice, and serve with cauli 'rice' or cauli wraps.

I ask the butcher to cut the brisket off the bone and to cut the bones into smaller pieces, but you can easily do this yourself after cooking if you're less lazy than I am.

Beef braciole

Serves 8

Fat 15g | Carbs 8g | Protein 41g

2 tbsp beef tallow
2 red onions, finely chopped
2 garlic cloves, crushed
6 anchovies, mashed
400g baby spinach
6 slices topside beef (about 1kg), thinly sliced and pounded
6 slices prosciutto
50g gruyère cheese, grated

FOR THE SAUCE
1 cup dry white wine
1 cup homemade beef stock
2 cups homemade passata
4 sprigs fresh rosemary
himalayan salt and black pepper

fresh bay leaves, to garnish

1. Heat 1 tbsp tallow in a pan, add the onion and sauté until soft. Toss in the garlic and sauté until golden; add the anchovies and spinach. Cook until the spinach wilts.
2. Put 3 beef slices on a surface slightly overlapping each other; top with 3 slices of prosciutto, and sprinkle with half the cheese and half the spinach mixture. Repeat these steps. Tightly roll up the slices as you would a swiss roll, and wrap snugly in muslin. Refrigerate for 30 minutes, then remove the muslin and secure the roll with string.
3. Preheat the oven to 150°C. On the stove top, heat a large ovenproof pot, add the remaining tallow and brown the meat roll on all sides.
4. For the sauce: Mix together the wine, beef stock and passata and pour over the meat. Add the rosemary and season well. Cover the pot and roast for 1 hour, then remove the cover and roast for an additional 20 minutes. Remove the beef from the pot and allow to rest for 10 minutes.
5. To serve: Remove the string and slice the roll into medallions. Serve with pan juices and garnish with bay leaves.

Rump steak with parmesan fried mushrooms

Serves 4

KEEP ON TRACK *per serving*

Fat 38g | Carbs 6g | Protein 49g

600g rump steak

FOR THE RUB
1 tsp smoked paprika
2 tsp celery salt
2 tsp crushed black pepper
1 tsp dried mustard
melted beef tallow, for brushing

FOR THE MUSHROOMS
250g button mushrooms
himalayan salt and black pepper
2 eggs, beaten
100g parmesan cheese, grated
5g flat-leaf parsley, chopped
pinch of dried chilli flakes
coconut oil, for frying

roasted red onion, to serve

1. Allow the meat to come to room temperature.
2. For the rub: Mix the spices together, brush the steak with tallow and sprinkle the spices over it. Allow to stand for 10 minutes.
3. Heat a griddle pan and cook the steak for 5 minutes, or until done to your liking, remove, set aside and allow to stand for 5 minutes before slicing.
4. For the mushrooms: Wipe the mushrooms and season well. Place the eggs in one small bowl and the parmesan, parsley and chilli in another.
5. Heat the coconut oil in a small pot. Dip the mushrooms first in the egg, then in the parmesan mixture, and place straight into the hot oil. Cook the mushrooms until golden, then drain on paper towel.
6. To serve: Serve steak with fried mushrooms and roasted red onion.

Beef bolognaise with zoodles

Serves 4

KEEP ON TRACK *per serving*

Fat 45g │ Carbs 19g │ Protein 38g

2 tbsp beef tallow
1 onion, finely chopped
2 garlic cloves, chopped
250g button mushrooms, sliced
600g beef mince
2 tbsp tomato paste
2 tsp xylitol
2 × 410g can italian chopped tomatoes
himalayan salt and black pepper
5g fresh basil
1 tbsp dried italian herbs

FOR THE ZOODLES
2 cups homemade chicken stock
6 courgettes, cut into zoodles (courgette 'noodles')
extra virgin olive oil, to drizzle

parmesan cheese, to serve

1. Heat the tallow in a pot, toss in the onion and garlic and sauté until golden.
2. Add the mushrooms and mince and cook until brown.
3. Stir in the tomato paste and xylitol and cook for 1 minute.
4. Pour in the canned tomato and bring to a simmer, cook for 20 minutes, season and add the herbs. Set aside.
5. For the zoodles: Heat the chicken stock in a pot to a simmer, add the courgettes and cook for 3 minutes, drain, drizzle with olive oil and season.
6. To serve: Toss zoodles with beef bolognaise, divide between 4 bowls, top with grated parmesan and serve immediately.

Beef chilli con carne with crispy eggplant

Serves 4

Fat 86g | Carbs 37g | Protein 35g

FOR THE CHILLI CON CARNE
2 tbsp beef tallow
2 garlic cloves
1 onion, finely diced
2–3 green chillies, finely sliced
1 tsp ground cumin
1 tsp ground coriander
600g beef mince
2 tbsp tomato paste
1 × 410g can chopped tomatoes
2 tsp xylitol
1 cup homemade beef stock
himalayan salt and black pepper

FOR THE EGGPLANT
¾ cup coconut oil, to fry
1 eggplant, thinly sliced
1 tsp ground coriander
1 tsp ground cumin

TO SERVE
guacamole, chopped tomato, fresh coriander and lime wedges

1. For the chilli con carne: Heat the tallow in a pan, add the garlic, onion, chilli and spices and sauté for 3 minutes, or until the onion is soft and golden. Add the mince and cook until browned, add tomato paste and cook for another minute, then stir in the remaining ingredients.
2. Bring to a boil, reduce the heat and simmer for 15 minutes. Season.
3. For the eggplant: Heat the oil in a small saucepan. Fry the eggplant slices until golden and crisp. Toss the spices together and sprinkle over the hot eggplant. Season to taste.
4. To serve: Place the mince in 4 bowls, and serve with eggplant, guacamole, tomato, coriander and lime wedges.

Beef and balsamic salad

Serves 2

per serving

Fat 50g | Carbs 24g | Protein 60g

400g beef fillet

FOR THE MARINADE
¼ cup balsamic vinegar
2 garlic cloves, crushed
¼ cup extra virgin olive oil
grated zest and juice of ½ lemon
pinch dried chilli flakes
himalayan salt and black pepper

FOR THE SALAD
1 red onion, thickly sliced
2 large red tomatoes, thickly sliced
1 tbsp xylitol
1 tbsp extra virgin olive oil
himalayan salt and black pepper

wild rocket, to serve

1. Preheat the oven to 200°C. Tie the fillet with string to help keep its shape or have your butcher prepare the meat.
2. For the marinade: In a bowl, whisk together the ingredients for the marinade, pour over the fillet and allow to marinate for 30 minutes.
3. For the salad: Arrange onion and tomato slices on a baking tray, sprinkle with xylitol and drizzle with olive oil. Season and roast for 30 minutes.
4. Heat a griddle pan until very hot. Remove fillet from the marinade, reserving the marinade, and cook fillet for 2 minutes on each side. Transfer fillet to a baking tray and place in the oven for 15 minutes.
5. Remove from the oven and allow fillet to rest for 10 minutes. Remove string and slice thinly.
6. Place reserved marinade in a small pot and bring to a simmer, reduce by half.
7. To serve: Arrange sliced fillet on a plate with roasted onion and tomato slices, and wild rocket leaves. Drizzle with marinade.

Peppered fillet with salsa verde

Serves 4–6

Fat 65g | Carbs 4g | Protein 80g

1.5kg beef fillet
1 tbsp beef tallow, melted
himalayan salt and black pepper
⅓ cup dijon mustard
3 tbsp pink peppercorns, lightly crushed

FOR THE SALSA VERDE
30g rocket, chopped
30g dill, chopped
30g basil leaves, chopped
2 anchovies, chopped
1 tsp dijon mustard
1 tbsp capers, chopped
juice of ½ lemon
½ cup extra virgin olive oil
himalayan salt and black pepper

1. Preheat the oven to 200°C. Brush fillet with melted tallow and season
well. Place a large frying pan over a high heat, sear the fillet on all sides until
browned, then remove and set aside.
2. Brush fillet with mustard and roll in pink peppercorns, place on a lined
baking tray and roast for 20 minutes. Remove and allow to stand for
20 minutes before slicing.
3. For the salsa verde: Mix together the rocket, dill, basil, anchovies, dijon
mustard and capers. Stir in the lemon juice and olive oil. Season.
4. To serve: Slice the fillet and serve with the salsa verde.

Eggplant rolls in a creamy tomato sauce

Serves 4–6

Fat 79g | Carbs 38g | Protein 48g

FOR THE TOMATO SAUCE
2 tbsp butter
1 tbsp extra virgin olive oil
1 red onion, finely chopped
150g bacon, chopped
2 × 410g cans cherry tomatoes
1 × 70g can tomato paste
big pinch dried chilli flakes
1 cup cream
himalayan salt and black pepper
5g fresh basil leaves, chopped

FOR THE FILLING
500g beef mince
100g feta cheese, crumbled
50g cream cheese
1 tsp dried rosemary
1½ tsp dried oregano
5g flat-leaf parsley, chopped

3 eggplants, finely sliced, brushed with extra virgin olive oil and grilled
50g parmesan cheese, grated, for sprinkling

1. For the sauce: Heat the butter and oil in a heavy-based pot over medium heat. Add the onion and bacon and sauté for about 4 minutes until golden. Add the tomatoes, tomato paste and chilli flakes. Simmer for 10 minutes.
2. Reduce the heat and stir in the cream. Simmer gently for 4 minutes, then season, stir in the basil, remove from the heat and allow to cool.
3. For the filling: Place all the ingredients in a bowl and stir well. Season to taste and roll into small balls. Preheat the oven to 190°C.
4. To assemble: Pour the sauce into an ovenproof dish. Place a meatball at the short end of each eggplant slice and roll up. Place the rolls in the sauce and top with a sprinkling of cheese. Cover with foil and bake for 30 minutes. Remove foil and bake for an extra 15 minutes, then sprinkle with more cheese and place under the grill for 2 minutes, or until golden and crispy.

Thai beef salad

Serves 4

Fat 51g | Carbs 10g | Protein 40g

700g beef rump steak

FOR THE MARINADE
20g fresh coriander
3 garlic cloves
1 lemongrass stalk, chopped
juice of 1 lime
1 tsp xylitol
himalayan salt and black pepper, to taste

FOR THE DRESSING
1 red chilli (optional)
2 green chillies
10g fresh mint
2 garlic cloves, chopped
juice of 2 limes
2 tsp xylitol
½ cup macadamia oil
2 tbsp fish sauce
50g salted almonds, toasted
30g fresh coriander, chopped

baby gem lettuce, to serve

1. Allow rump to come to room temperature.
2. For the marinade: Place the marinade ingredients in a blender and blitz until smooth. Pour over the meat; allow to stand for 30 minutes.
3. For the dressing: Blitz the ingredients in a blender and set aside.
4. Heat a griddle pan until very hot, place the meat on the pan and cook for 4–5 minutes on each side, or until done to your liking. Remove, allow to rest for 5 minutes and slice.
5. To serve: Place baby gem leaves on a platter, top with the sliced rump and pour the dressing over the top.

Beef pot roast with mushroom gravy

Serves 8–10

KEEP ON TRACK *per serving*

Fat 63g | Carbs 15g | Protein 48g

¼ cup beef tallow
2kg silverside, chuck, blade or brisket (well-marbled cuts are the most tender)
¼ cup wholegrain mustard
12 baby onions
2 large carrots, peeled and cut in half
1 cup dry red wine
2 cups homemade beef stock
a few sprigs of rosemary
himalayan salt and black pepper

FOR THE MUSHROOM GRAVY
1 tbsp beef tallow
250g portabellini mushrooms, sliced
2 tbsp almond flour

flat-leaf parsley, to garnish

1. Preheat the oven to 160°C. Melt the tallow in a large ovenproof pot with a lid, and brown the beef on all sides. Remove and spread with mustard.
2. Place onions in a bowl, cover with boiling water, allow to stand for 5 minutes, then peel.
3. Arrange the beef in the centre of the pot, surrounded by the onions and carrots. It should be a snug fit.
4. Add the wine, stock and rosemary to the pot and season. Cover with tin foil and the lid of the pot. Place in the oven and cook for 3 hours.
5. Remove the beef and vegetables and strain the cooking liquid into a jug.
6. For the gravy: Melt the tallow in a small pot and fry the mushrooms. Add the almond flour and cook for 2 minutes before adding 2 cups of cooking liquid from the pot roast. Simmer until the sauce thickens. Season.
7. To serve: Slice the roast and serve with the vegetables and mushroom gravy. Garnish with parsley.

Italian-style beef short ribs

Serves 4

KEEP ON TRACK *per serving*

Fat 65g | Carbs 25g | Protein 55g

800g beef short ribs, trimmed
himalayan salt and black pepper
1 tbsp beef tallow or coconut oil

FOR THE SAUCE
1 tbsp beef tallow or coconut oil
3 leeks, chopped
100g pancetta, chopped
2 sweet red peppers, chopped
3 stalks celery, chopped
3 garlic cloves, chopped
2 cups homemade passata
½ cup dry white wine
1 cup homemade beef stock
3 bay leaves
100g green olives, drained

cauli 'mash', to serve
rocket, to garnish

1. Place the ribs on a board and season well.
2. Heat the tallow in a pan, brown the ribs on all sides, then remove from
the pan and set aside.
3. For the sauce: Heat the remaining tallow in a pot, add the leek,
pancetta, sweet pepper and celery and sauté till softened. Add garlic
and sauté for another minute. Add the remaining sauce ingredients,
plus the ribs, and bring to a boil. Reduce heat and simmer very gently
for 2 hours.
4. To serve: Serve with cauli 'mash' and garnish with rocket.

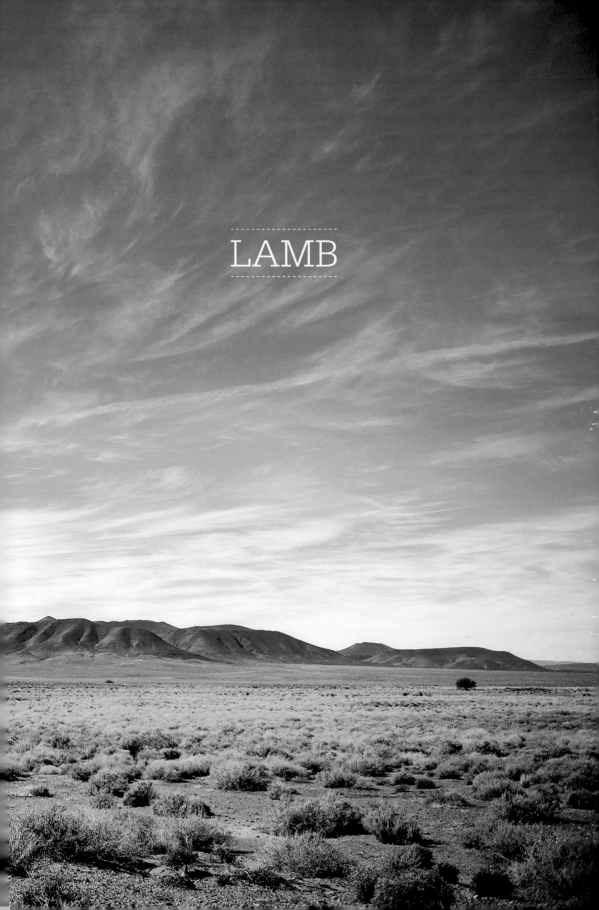

LAMB

Tagine of lamb shanks

Serves 6

per serving

Fat 40g | Carbs 19g | Protein 99g

6 lamb shanks
himalayan salt and black pepper
coconut oil or lamb tallow, for frying
2 onions, sliced
2 garlic cloves, chopped
3 sticks cinnamon
1 tsp ground ginger
100g almonds, chopped
big pinch saffron in a little hot water
2 wedges preserved lemon (pith removed), chopped
2 tbsp xylitol
3–4 cups lamb or beef stock
500g pumpkin, cubed

cauli 'rice', to serve

1. Place the lamb on a board and season well. Heat the oil in a large, deep pot. Brown the lamb on all sides, then remove from the pot.
2. Toss in the onion, garlic and dry spices and sauté until golden, then add the almonds and sauté until just browned. Return the lamb shanks to the pot and add the remaining ingredients (except for the pumpkin). Bring to a boil, then reduce the heat and simmer for 2 hours, adding more stock if necessary.
3. Half an hour before the end of cooking time, add the pumpkin and season to taste.
4. To serve: Serve shanks hot with cauli 'rice'.

Sunday lunch leg of lamb

Serves 6–8

KEEP ON TRACK *per serving*

Fat 77g │ Carbs 14g │ Protein 59g

FOR THE MARINADE
½ cup extra virgin olive oil
100g capers, drained, roughly chopped
½ tsp dried chilli flakes, crushed
grated zest and juice of 2 lemons
1 tbsp fennel seeds, toasted and crushed
himalayan salt and black pepper

1 × 2kg leg of lamb, deboned, shank bone left in
10 garlic cloves, peeled
3 pimento peppers, deseeded and sliced
1 orange, cut into wedges

FOR MINT AND YOGHURT SAUCE
½ cup fresh mint leaves, chopped
1 cup double cream yoghurt
½ red onion, chopped

1. For the marinade: In a small bowl, mix together the olive oil, capers, chilli flakes, lemon zest and juice, and fennel seeds, and season to taste.
2. Stud the lamb with garlic cloves, then place in a baking dish. Pour the marinade over the lamb and marinate for 1 hour.
3. Preheat the oven to 180°C. Add the pimento peppers and orange wedges to the baking dish. Cover with foil and roast for 1 hour, remove foil and roast for another half hour, or until done to your liking.
4. For the mint and yoghurt sauce: Mix together all the ingredients and season well.
5. Remove the lamb from the oven. Allow to rest for 20 minutes before slicing.
6. To serve: Slice lamb and serve with mint and yoghurt sauce.

Italian-style lamb casserole

Serves 4–6

KEEP ON TRACK *per serving*

Fat 101g | Carbs 31g | Protein 96g

2kg lamb neck on the bone, cut into rings
himalayan salt and black pepper
1 tbsp almond flour
1 tbsp lard
1 red onion, finely diced
4 garlic cloves, crushed
12 anchovies
10 caper berries
pinch dried chilli flakes, crushed
2 × 410g cans cherry tomatoes
1 cup homemade chicken stock
1 cup dry white wine
50g black olives, pitted
350g vine tomatoes
10g flat-leaf parsley, chopped

extra flat-leaf parsley, to serve

1. Season the lamb, then toss it in the almond flour. Heat the lard in a heavy-based pot and brown the lamb. Remove and drain on paper towel.
2. Remove excess fat from the pot; add the onion and sauté until soft. Add the garlic, anchovies and caper berries, and sauté for another minute. Return the lamb to the pot, add the chilli flakes and stir in the canned tomatoes, chicken stock, wine and olives. Place the lid on the pot and simmer for 2 hours.
3. Remove the lid, add the vine tomatoes and continue to cook over a low heat, covered, for another 20 minutes, or until the tomatoes have softened. Season and stir in the chopped parsley.
4. To serve: Sprinkle with extra parsley and serve hot.

Lamb shanks in a rich tomato sauce

Serves 6

Fat 71g | Carbs 31g | Protein 72g

6 lamb shanks
1 cup coconut flour with 1 tsp smoked paprika
2 tbsp extra virgin olive oil
4 tbsp butter/coconut oil
3 garlic cloves, finely chopped
6–8 baby onions, peeled
2 carrots, peeled and cut into chunks
8 anchovies, chopped
1 tbsp dried rosemary
2 bay leaves
big pinch dried chilli flakes, crushed
2 tbsp tomato paste
3 × 410g cans cherry tomatoes
1½ cups dry red wine
sea salt and black pepper, to taste
handful of flat-leaf parsley, chopped

cauli 'mash' to serve

1. Allow the shanks to come to room temperature. Toss in the seasoned flour and set aside.
2. Heat 1 tbsp olive oil and 1 tbsp butter in a large ovenproof pot. Add the lamb shanks, brown on all sides and remove. Wipe out the pot with paper towel.
3. Preheat the oven to 160°C. Add the remaining olive oil and butter to the pot, toss in the garlic, onions and carrot and sauté until lightly golden. Add the anchovies, rosemary, bay leaves and chilli flakes and cook for another minute, stirring occasionally. Return the lamb shanks to the pot; stir to combine. Add the remaining ingredients, except for the parsley, and bring to a boil, then remove from the hob, cover and place in the oven. Cook for 2 hours, adding more wine, if necessary. Remove from the oven and stir in the parsley.
4. To serve: Serve shanks with cauli 'mash'.

Lamb and eggplant bakes

Serves 4

KEEP ON TRACK *per serving*

Fat 44g | Carbs 18g | Protein 38g

2 eggplants, thinly sliced
coarse salt, for sprinkling
macadamia oil, for drizzling
1 tbsp beef tallow/duck fat
1 onion, finely chopped
2 garlic cloves, chopped
500g lamb mince
2 tsp ground coriander
½ tsp dried chilli flakes
2 tbsp tomato paste
2 × 410g cans chopped tomato
2 tsp xylitol
1 tsp dried oregano or rosemary
himalayan salt and black pepper
50g parmesan cheese, grated

1. Sprinkle coarse salt onto the eggplant slices and allow to stand in a colander for 30 minutes. Rinse the salt off the eggplant and pat dry. Preheat the oven grill, drizzle the eggplant with macadamia oil and grill on both sides until golden. Set aside.
2. Heat the tallow in the pan, add the onion and garlic and sauté until golden; add the mince, coriander and chilli flakes and brown. Add the tomato paste and cook for 1 minute, add the chopped tomato, xylitol and herbs. Allow to simmer for 30 minutes, then season.
3. Preheat the oven to 180°C.
4. To assemble: Place a layer of eggplant on the base of a baking dish, followed by a layer of mince; continue with these layers until you have used all the mixture.
5. Sprinkle with parmesan cheese. Bake for 30 minutes.
6. To serve: Serve hot with extra parmesan.

Harissa lamb kebabs with balsamic onions

Serves 4

KEEP ON TRACK *per serving*

Fat 38g | Carbs 7g | Protein 32g

FOR THE KEBABS
1 tbsp harissa paste
½ tsp smoked paprika
1 tbsp coconut oil, melted
himalayan salt and black pepper, to taste
700g lamb cubes (we used leg
of lamb)

FOR THE ONIONS
1 tbsp coconut oil
2 red onions, sliced
1 tbsp xylitol
2 tbsp balsamic vinegar

TO SERVE
double cream yoghurt
baby spinach salad

1. For the kebabs: Mix together the harissa paste, paprika, coconut oil and seasoning and rub this mixture over the lamb cubes. Set aside.
2. For the onions: Heat the coconut oil in a heavy-based pot, toss in the onion, xylitol and vinegar and cook over a low heat, covered, for 10–15 minutes.
3. In the meantime, thread the lamb onto skewers and cook under a preheated grill until done to your liking.
4. To serve: Divide the kebabs between 4 plates, top with a dollop of yoghurt and caramelised onion, and serve with a baby spinach salad.

Lamb loin chops with red pepper and walnut dip

Serves 4

KEEP ON TRACK *per serving*

Fat 36g | Carbs 14g | Protein 51g

FOR THE LAMB CHOPS
8 lamb loin chops
2 tsp dried thyme
himalayan salt and black pepper

FOR THE DIP
2 red peppers, roasted and peeled
1 small garlic clove, crushed
¼ onion, finely chopped
70g walnuts, toasted and chopped
1 tsp each ground cumin, coriander and paprika
juice of ½ lemon
pinch dried chilli flakes
1–2 tbsp xylitol
2 tbsp butter, melted
1 tbsp double cream yoghurt

FOR THE SALAD
50g pomegranate rubies
3 courgettes, sliced into thin strips
½ red onion, cut into wedges
extra virgin olive oil, to drizzle
1 tsp lemon juice

1. For the lamb chops: Preheat the oven grill or a griddle pan. Place the lamb chops on a board, sprinkle with thyme and season well, then thread them onto skewers and grill until done to your liking. Set aside.
2. For the dip: Place all the ingredients, except for the yoghurt, in a food processor and blitz well. Place in a bowl, season and top with yoghurt.
3. For the salad: Toss the salad ingredients together, place on a platter and drizzle with olive oil and lemon juice.
4. To serve: Serve the lamb hot with the dip and salad.

Spicy double lamb patties on banting wraps

Serves 4

KEEP ON TRACK *per serving*

Fat 45g | Carbs 14g | Protein 43g

FOR THE PATTIES
600g lamb mince
2 green chillies, seeded and chopped
2 garlic cloves, crushed
70g feta, crumbled
10g fresh coriander leaves, chopped
1 tbsp ground coriander
himalayan salt and black pepper
2 tbsp beef or lamb tallow, for frying

FOR THE PICKLED ONIONS
1 tbsp vinegar
2 tsp xylitol
1 red onion, finely sliced

TO SERVE
banting wraps, lettuce, sliced tomatoes, double cream yoghurt and fresh herbs

1. For the patties: Place all the ingredients, except the tallow, in a bowl, season well and stir to combine. Divide the mixture into 8 patties, heat the tallow in a frying pan and cook the patties until done to your liking. Remove and keep warm.
2. For the pickled onions: In a small bowl, mix together the vinegar and xylitol, add 2 tbsp water and toss in the onion. Allow to stand for 10 minutes.
3. To assemble: Heat the wraps according to packet instructions, top with lettuce, tomato, patties and pickled onion.
4. To serve: Serve immediately with a dollop of double cream yoghurt and a sprinkling of fresh herbs.

PORK

SHARON VAN WYK

Half-marathon runner

'When I reached 37, the years of infertility treatments, miscarriages and depression had taken their toll on my health and weight – I was tipping the scales at 118kg. I'd spent a fortune on diet pills, diet shakes, dieticians and every crazy fad diet imaginable. Nothing worked. I'd lose a couple of kilos, but be hungry and miserable the entire time. In addition, I found out I was insulin resistant. I was concerned about my ballooning weight and its effect on my health because I want to see my girls grow up. When my best friend lost 22kg with banting, I decided to give it a try. In the first month, I lost 8.8kg and almost immediately started to notice differences in my health and wellbeing. My IBS [irritable bowel syndrome] vanished almost overnight, my knees and feet were pain-free for the first time in years, I started sleeping better, and I didn't feel sleepy or lethargic all day and had no mid-afternoon slumps. Almost 11 months into banting, I'd lost a total of 32kg. Aside from my drastically decreased waistline, I started running because my energy levels had improved and the pain in my body had vanished. Thanks to banting, I've now maintained my weight for two years and run multiple half marathons! We eat simple foods: lots of vegetables, salads, eggs and a small portion of meat at most meals. I'm still loving it – my husband and daughters too. It's life-changing. I will never look back.'

Sharon's pork loin stir-fry

Serves 4

Fat 13g | Carbs 13g | Protein 30g

1 tbsp coconut oil
500g pork loin, deboned, cut into strips
1 sweet red pepper, sliced
4 red spring onions, sliced
200g extra-fine green beans

FOR THE SAUCE
2 tsp chinese 5-spice
60ml coconut water
juice of 1 lime

8 baby pak choi
500g zoodles (courgette 'noodles'), blanched, to serve

1. Heat the coconut oil in a pan on high heat. Add the pork loin strips and lightly brown. Remove from the pan.
2. Add the sliced pepper, spring onion and green beans to the pan and cook for a minute.
3. Combine the ingredients for the sauce, add to the pan and return the pork strips to cook for a minute while stirring.
4. Add the pak choi just before removing from the heat to warm through.
5. To serve: Serve with blanched zoodles.

Gammon with raspberry glaze

Serves 10–12

KEEP ON TRACK *per serving*

Fat 28g | Carbs 3g | Protein 70g

1 × smoked cooked gammon, about 3–4kg, bone in
cloves, for studding

FOR THE GLAZE
200g raspberries
2 cinnamon sticks
30g xylitol

wholegrain mustard, to serve

1. Carefully remove the skin from the gammon and gently score the
fat in a diamond pattern, studding each diamond with a clove.
2. For the glaze: Place the ingredients in a pot, stir over a medium
heat until the xylitol dissolves, then bring to a boil, reduce the heat
and simmer for 3 minutes. Remove from the heat and allow to cool.
3. Preheat the oven to 200°C. Brush the glaze over the gammon fat
and cook for 20–30 minutes, or until golden, brushing the gammon
at intervals with any remaining glaze. Remove from the oven and
allow to cool.
4. To serve: Slice the gammon and serve with wholegrain mustard.

Warm paprika pork fillet with apple salad

Serves 4

KEEP ON TRACK *per serving*

Fat 46g | Carbs 18g | Protein 46g

2 tbsp extra virgin olive oil
2 tsp smoked paprika
juice of 1 lemon
himalayan salt and black pepper
800g pork fillet
2 tbsp coconut oil

FOR THE DRESSING
2 tsp red wine vinegar
2 tsp wholegrain mustard
⅓ cup extra virgin olive oil
pinch of crushed dried chillies

TO SERVE
½ head red cabbage, shredded or cut into wedges
1 green apple, sliced
1 head endive, leaves separated
75g pomegranate rubies
10g fresh mint

1. Rub olive oil, paprika, lemon juice, salt and pepper into the pork fillet.
2. Preheat the oven to 180°C. Heat the coconut oil in an ovenproof pan and sear the pork on all sides. Place in the oven and roast for 15 minutes. Remove and allow to cool for 5 minutes, then slice.
3. For the dressing: Place the vinegar and mustard in a small jug, whisk in the olive oil, add the chillies and season to taste.
4. To serve: Place the cabbage, apple and endive on a platter, top with the pork and drizzle with the dressing. Garnish with pomegranate rubies and fresh mint.

Pork sausages with pancetta

Serves 4

KEEP ON TRACK *per serving*

Fat 60g | Carbs 3g | Protein 35g

8 thin slices pancetta, approximately 100g
8 pork sausages
5g fresh sage
2 tbsp lard
2 tsp xylitol
himalayan salt and black pepper

sage leaves, to garnish
dijon mustard, to serve

1. Preheat the oven to 180°C. Wrap the pancetta around the sausages and thread the sausages and sage leaves onto pre-soaked kebab sticks.
2. Heat a small frying pan over a medium heat, add the lard and allow to melt. Add the xylitol, stir until dissolved and season. Brush this mixture over the sausages and bake for 10–15 minutes, turning and brushing frequently.
3. To serve: Garnish the sausages with sage leaves and serve with mustard.

Roast pork belly with crispy crackling

Serves 6-8

Fat 71g | Carbs 12g | Protein 41g

1.5kg pork belly, unrolled
2 tbsp himalayan salt flakes
2 garlic cloves, crushed
2 tbsp chopped parsley
2 tbsp chopped sage
black pepper
1 red onion, cut into 8 wedges
100g baby leeks
4 long stalks celery
5g fresh sage leaves
1½ cups homemade vegetable stock or dry white wine

roasted baby savoy cabbages and red onions, to serve

1. Pat the skin of the pork belly dry with paper towel; never wash the pork under running water.
2. Once the skin is as dry as possible, rub it with plenty of salt, then refrigerate for a couple of hours.
3. Preheat the oven to 220°C. Combine the garlic, parsley and sage and rub over the underside of the meat. Season with a little salt and pepper.
4. Arrange the onion, leeks and celery in a roasting pan and top with the pork belly, skin-side up. Scatter sage leaves over the top. Roast for 35 minutes or until crackling begins to blister and turn golden, then add the stock and reduce the heat to 190°C. Roast for a further 1–1½ hours or until crackling is crisp and the meat is tender.
5. To serve: Slice the pork and serve with roasted baby savoy cabbages and red onions.

Balsamic pork neck braise

Serves 4

KEEP ON TRACK *per serving*

Fat 89g | Carbs 25g | Protein 62g

1.2kg pork neck, sliced
himalayan salt and black pepper
2 tbsp lard
100g chorizo sausage, sliced
1 onion, finely sliced
2 garlic cloves, chopped
100g green olives, drained
2 tsp smoked paprika
2 tbsp balsamic vinegar
90g can tomato paste
2 bay leaves
1 tbsp oregano
2 × 410g cans whole tomatoes
1 cup homemade beef stock

flat-leaf parsley, to garnish
grilled vine tomatoes, to serve

1. Allow the pork neck to come to room temperature. Season well. Heat the lard in a heavy-based pot (with a lid) and brown the pork well on all sides. Remove the pork from the pot and set aside.
2. Add the chorizo to the pot and fry until crispy; set aside. Sauté onion and garlic until golden. Return chorizo to the pot; add the olives, paprika, vinegar, tomato paste, bay leaves and oregano and cook for 1 minute. Return the pork to the pot, add canned tomatoes and stock, and season.
3. Replace the lid and cook for 1½ hours on low. Remove the lid and simmer for 20 minutes more.
4. To serve: Sprinkle with parsley and serve with grilled vine tomatoes.

Warm tomato and pork stir-fry with courgette noodles

Serves 4

KEEP ON TRACK *per serving*

Fat 24g | **Carbs 11g** | **Protein 30g**

500g pork fillet, sliced
2 tsp thai 7-spice
3 tbsp coconut oil
1 × 5cm piece ginger, chopped
2 garlic cloves, chopped
2 spring onions, sliced
1 stalk lemongrass, finely chopped
300g mixed cherry tomatoes
1 × 165ml can coconut milk
2 tbsp lime juice
himalayan salt and black pepper
4 courgettes, cut into julienne strips

fresh coriander and baby gem lettuce, to serve

1. Toss the pork fillet with the 7-spice and set aside.
2. Heat 1 tbsp coconut oil in a wok over a high heat, add the pork and stir-fry until crisp and golden. Remove pork and set aside.
3. Add another tablespoonful of coconut oil to the wok, toss in the ginger, garlic, spring onion and lemongrass and sauté until golden.
4. Add the tomatoes, cook for a minute, then add the coconut milk and bring to a boil. Simmer for 2 minutes.
5. Add the pork and lime juice and season to taste. Keep warm.
6. Heat the remaining tablespoonful of coconut oil in a pan or wok, add the courgette strips, season and cook until crispy.
7. To serve: Divide courgette 'noodles' between 4 serving bowls, top with tomato pork stir-fry and serve with coriander and lettuce leaves.

Pizzas with roast garlic and shredded pork

Serves 4

KEEP ON TRACK *per serving*

Fat 78g │ Carbs 26g │ Protein 57g

800g pork belly, cut in half
1 tbsp himalayan salt
1 tbsp black pepper
3 cups homemade chicken stock
3 star anise
2 cinnamon sticks
1 head garlic
350g vine tomatoes
4 readymade pumpkin wraps or cauli pizza bases
¾ cup crème fraîche

extra virgin olive oil, to drizzle
fresh basil, to garnish

1. Preheat the oven to 200°C.
2. Season the pork with salt and pepper and place in a small, deep ovenproof dish. Pour over the stock, add the star anise and cinnamon sticks and cover with foil. Cook for 1 hour, then switch off the oven and leave the pork in the oven to cool.
3. While cooking the pork, wrap the garlic head in foil, place on a small baking tray and roast in the oven for 30 minutes. Remove from the oven and allow to cool, then open the foil, cut open the cloves and set aside.
4. When the pork is cool, remove it from the dish, reserve the cooking liquid and some of the fat, shred the pork and set aside.
5. Heat a large frying pan, add the reserved pork fat to the pan, toss in the tomatoes and cook for 1 minute. Add the shredded pork and ½ cup of the reserved cooking liquid and simmer gently for 3–4 minutes or until the pork is heated through and the tomatoes have softened.
6. To assemble: Heat wraps, place on a surface, then spread with crème fraîche and top with shredded pork, vine tomatoes and roasted garlic segments.
7. To serve: Drizzle with a little olive oil, scatter basil over the top and serve immediately.

Spinach and feta-filled pork chops
Serves 6

KEEP ON TRACK per serving

Fat 47g | Carbs 6g | Protein 49g

FOR THE STUFFING
1 tsp pork lard
100g baby spinach, chopped
60g cream cheese
50g feta, crumbled
5g fresh sage, chopped
freshly grated nutmeg
himalayan salt and black pepper

6 thick-cut (about 3 cm) pork loin chops
2 tsp dried rosemary
2 tbsp pork lard

wild rocket and pomegranate rubies, to garnish
350g mixed tomatoes, pan-fried

1. For the stuffing: Heat a small frying pan, add the lard, allow to melt, then toss in the spinach and cook until just wilted. Remove and place in a bowl to cool. Add the cream cheese, feta, sage and nutmeg. Season well and stir to combine.
2. Preheat the oven to 180°C. Place the pork chops on a surface. Using a small knife, cut a deep 'pocket' into the loin section of each chop. Spoon 2 tbsp of stuffing into the pocket of each chop.
3. Secure the stuffed pockets with toothpicks and tie or link the toothpicks with kitchen string. Season the chops well and sprinkle with dried rosemary.
4. Heat the lard in a large frying pan, add 2–3 chops at a time and cook on both sides until golden. Place the chops on a roasting tray and roast in the oven for 10–15 minutes or until cooked through. Remove from the oven and allow to rest, covered with foil, for 5 minutes. Remove toothpicks and string before serving.
5. To serve: Garnish the chops with rocket and pomegranate rubies and serve with pan-fried tomatoes.

Breaking
the fast

SHANNON MCLAUGHLIN

New mother and inspired entrepreneur

'The day I found out I was pregnant marked exactly 10 months of being completely sugar, wheat and grain-free. I followed a low-carb diet throughout my pregnancy – and had no morning sickness at all! I felt really well throughout – as did my baby, who arrived two weeks later than anticipated, at a whopping 4.1kg.

'It's now two years since Leo was born, and we are all doing extremely well. I still follow a low-carb diet 90 percent of the time (occasionally a busy mom just has to have a cup of coffee and a rusk). I gained 14kg during my pregnancy, and lost it all within a month of Leo's arrival. I'm sure breastfeeding helped, but it was primarily down to eating low carbs and healthy fats. One of the things I love most about it is that it's such an easy way to eat – you really don't need to be a brilliant cook.

'I felt healthy and energetic throughout my pregnancy and was able to carry Leo for 42 weeks and still go for a walk every day. I think that's quite remarkable, considering how enormous my tummy was. And I'd most definitely eat that way again second time around!'

http://ubuntubaba.com

Shannon's green omelette

Serves 2

KEEP ON TRACK *per serving*

Fat 31g | Carbs 11g | Protein 33g

6 jumbo eggs
1 tsp dijon mustard
himalayan salt and black pepper
1 tbsp coconut oil

FOR THE FILLING
2 spring onions, chopped
10g flat-leaf parsley, chopped
30g baby spinach, shredded
50g goat's cheese, crumbled

chopped tomato and herbs, to serve

1. Place the eggs in a bowl, add 2 tbsp water and the mustard and season well, whisk until combined.
2. Heat a little coconut oil in a frying pan, add half the egg mixture and swirl around the pan to cover the base, allow to partially set.
3. For the filling: Combine all the filling ingredients and sprinkle half of the filling over one side of the omelette. Fold the 'empty' side over the filling, slide out of the pan onto a plate and keep warm.
4. Repeat with the remaining coconut oil, egg mixture and filling.
5. To serve: Serve omelettes topped with chopped tomato and herbs.

Smoked salmon eggs benedict on banting röstis

Serves 4

per serving

Fat 59g | Carbs 37g | Protein 19g

FOR THE RÖSTIS
3 red sweet potatoes, peeled and grated
½ red onion, finely sliced
1 garlic clove, crushed
1 egg, beaten
1 tbsp psyllium husks
2 tbsp finely chopped parsley, plus extra to garnish
himalayan salt and black pepper, to taste
2 tbsp extra virgin olive oil
2 tbsp butter

FOR THE HOLLANDAISE
2 large egg yolks
1 tbsp white balsamic vinegar
¾ cup butter, melted

TO SERVE
100g smoked salmon or ham
4 poached eggs
dill and micro greens, to garnish

1. For the röstis: Combine all the ingredients, except the oil and butter, in a bowl.
2. Heat the oil and butter in a large nonstick frying pan.
3. Place large tablespoonfuls of the rösti mixture into the pan and cook over a low heat for about 8 minutes, turning every 2 minutes, until the röstis are a dark golden-brown colour and cooked through. Remove and keep warm.
4. For the hollandaise: Place egg yolks and vinegar in a bowl over a bain-marie and whisk until pale. Slowly add the melted butter until a thick sauce is formed, season and keep warm. The sauce can be thinned with 3–4 tbsp boiling water if desired.
5. To serve: Serve röstis topped with salmon or ham, poached eggs and hollandaise, and garnished with dill and micro greens.

Mushroom pâté served with crisp poppy seed crackers

Serves 4

KEEP ON TRACK *per serving*

Fat 45g | Carbs 19g | Protein 14g

FOR THE CRACKERS
1½ cups almond flour
1 tbsp poppy seeds
2 tbsp extra virgin olive oil
¼ tsp coarse salt
1 large egg white, lightly beaten

FOR THE MUSHROOM PÂTÉ
2 tbsp butter
1 tbsp extra virgin olive oil
1 onion, chopped
3 garlic cloves, crushed
250g portabellini mushrooms, roughly chopped
½ cup dry white wine (optional)
1 tbsp chopped fresh thyme leaves
120g cream cheese
himalayan salt and black pepper

1. For the crackers: Preheat the oven to 180°C. Combine flour, poppy seeds, oil, salt and egg white. Transfer the mixture to a greased foil-lined baking sheet.
2. Cover with baking paper and roll out to a rectangle about 30×20cm. Remove the baking paper and cut into 16 crackers. Bake for 15 minutes until golden brown. Leave to cool.
3. For the pâté: Melt the butter and olive oil in a frying pan, add the onion and garlic and fry until soft and golden. Add the mushrooms and white wine and cook over a high heat until all the wine has evaporated. Remove from the heat and add the thyme and cream cheese and season with salt and pepper.
4. Place the mixture in a blender and pulse until smooth.
5. To serve: Place the pâté in a bowl and serve with the crackers.

Smoked salmon, leek, dill and cream cheese frittata with roasted caprese-stuffed tomatoes

Serves 4

KEEP ON TRACK *per serving*

Fat 83g | Carbs 60g | Protein 44g

FOR THE STUFFED TOMATOES
6 large vine tomatoes
300g bocconcini (little mozzarella balls)
½ cup homemade basil pesto
himalayan salt and black pepper

FOR THE FRITTATA
1 tsp extra virgin olive oil
3 leeks, thinly sliced
10 large eggs
230g cream cheese
1 cup cream
100g smoked salmon or rainbow trout
2g dill sprigs

1. Preheat the oven to 180°C and grease a 22cm-diameter ovenproof dish or quiche tin with coconut oil.
2. For the tomatoes: Carefully cut the top off each tomato and scoop out the seeds. Stuff each tomato with 3 bocconcini, add a dollop of pesto and season well. Replace the top of each tomato and arrange the tomatoes on a baking tray.
3. For the frittata: Heat the oil in a pan and fry the leeks until golden and soft. Remove from the heat and set aside.
4. Place the eggs, cream cheese and cream in a bowl and whisk well until smooth. Season well.
5. Pour the egg mixture into the ovenproof dish and arrange the leeks and smoked salmon on top.
6. Bake for 30 minutes, then put the tomatoes into the oven and cook for another 30 minutes until the tomatoes are cooked and the frittata has set in the centre.
7. To serve: Serve the frittata warm with the stuffed tomatoes.

breaking the fast

Sage, onion and pork scotch eggs

Makes 6 scotch eggs

KEEP ON TRACK *per serving*

Fat 72g | Carbs 10g | Protein 31g

6 large eggs, boiled for 4 minutes and chilled
1 tbsp extra virgin olive oil
1 onion, finely chopped
3 garlic cloves, crushed
2 tbsp finely chopped fresh sage
3 tbsp finely chopped flat-leaf parsley
2 tbsp finely chopped fresh thyme
500g pork mince
himalayan salt and black pepper
1½ cups almond or coconut flour, for coating
2 eggs, beaten
1 cup coconut oil, for frying

1. Carefully peel the cold eggs and set aside.
2. Heat the olive oil in a frying pan and fry the onion until golden, add the garlic and herbs and set aside to cool.
3. Combine the cooled onion mixture with the pork and season well.
4. Divide the mixture into 6 equal balls. Place a pork ball onto a piece of lightly oiled baking paper and gently press out into a 15–20cm circle. Place an egg on top of the mince and, using the paper, carefully wrap the mince up and around the egg to enclose it. Gently peel off the paper and shape the ball to create an even layer of mince around the egg. Repeat the process with the remaining eggs and mince. Place on a plate and chill for 1 hour.
5. Roll each scotch egg in the almond or coconut flour, then in the beaten egg and again in the flour until well coated.
6. Preheat the oven to 180°C. Melt the coconut oil in a frying pan and fry the eggs until golden brown, then arrange on a baking tray and cook for a further 15 minutes.
7. To serve: Serve the scotch eggs warm or at room temperature.

Coconut, goji berry and macadamia bars

Makes 12 bars

per serving

Fat 23g | Carbs 11g | Protein 6g

½ cup almond or macadamia nut butter
¼ cup melted coconut oil
1 egg, beaten
½ cup xylitol
1 tbsp vanilla extract
½ tsp himalayan salt
½ tsp ground cinnamon
½ cup desiccated coconut
¾ cup coconut flour
½ cup coconut milk
100g macadamia nuts, ground
¼ cup dried goji berries

80% dark chocolate, melted, to drizzle

1. Preheat oven to 170°C.
2. Place all the ingredients, except the chocolate, in a blender and pulse until well combined.
3. Press the mixture into a greased and lined 22cm square baking tin and bake for 35–40 minutes until pale golden. Leave to cool completely before slicing into bars.
4. To serve: Drizzle bars with melted dark chocolate and serve with black tea or coffee with cream.

Nut and dairy free

REYHANA THUMBRAN

Certified wellness and banting coach

'Before starting to eat LCHF, I was overweight, hungry and tired all the time. After three consecutive pregnancies, I weighed 105kg. The eating plan the dietician had given me left me feeling hungry and miserable. It also took a long time to lose very little weight. I'll never forget the moment the doctor turned to me with a solemn look and asked, "How long have you had diabetes?" Confused, my heart began to race. "Diabetes?" I asked. He then informed me that my blood glucose was 16.9mmol (normal is around 4.5). Suddenly I felt like I'd lost a battle I didn't even know I was fighting. After researching the disease, I realised every road ended with the banting diet as the only hope, so I decided to try it. In just five months, I lost 20kg and went from a size 40 to a 36. My blood glucose is now stable, at 3.8mmol. My general health started to improve: my skin glowed, I no longer needed antacids for acid reflux, I slept well and woke up feeling vibrant and full of energy. Not only do I feel great – and confident – but I'm no longer hungry and I'm free of my sugar addiction. All I'm addicted to is life, in abundance!'

Reyhana's lamb curry

Serves 4

KEEP ON TRACK *per serving*

Fat 50g | Carbs 21g | Protein 47g

1 tsp cumin seeds
1½ tbsp ghee
1 onion, sliced
7 whole peppercorns
4 whole cardamom pods
2 cinnamon sticks
5 whole cloves
1 tbsp each chopped fresh garlic and ginger
1kg leg of lamb or mutton
1½ tsp himalayan salt
¼ tsp turmeric
2 tsp normal red masala mix
2½ tsp ground cumin
2 level tbsp ground coriander
4 tsp red chilli powder
2 medium tomatoes, grated
3 small sweet potatoes (optional)

5g fresh coriander, chopped
chopped cucumber and red onion, and lemon zest, to garnish
chopped tomato, cucumber and red onion salad, to serve

1. Place the cumin seeds in a pot, dry-fry until browned, then add the ghee and toss in the onion, peppercorns, cardamom pods, cinnamon sticks and whole cloves. Stir to combine, then add the garlic and ginger. Add meat and braise, season with salt and add the turmeric.
2. Add enough water to cover, and cook until the meat is tender, about 30 minutes, and the liquid is reduced.
3. Add masala, cumin, coriander and chilli powder, cook for a minute and then add the grated tomato and simmer for about 10 minutes on low heat. Add potatoes and a cup of boiling water and cook until soft.
4. To serve: Add chopped coriander and garnish with chopped cucumber and red onion, and lemon zest. Serve with a salad of chopped tomato, cucumber and red onion mixed with a little salt and lemon juice.

Massaged kale, caramelised onion, roasted pumpkin and vine tomato salad

Serves 4–6

KEEP ON TRACK *per serving*

Fat 37g | Carbs 31g | Protein 8g

300g kale, deveined and finely chopped
juice of ½ lemon
1 tsp sea salt flakes
2 tbsp extra virgin olive oil, plus extra for drizzling
300g pumpkin, sliced into wedges
himalayan salt and black pepper
400g vine tomatoes
3 tbsp pumpkin seeds
3 tbsp butter
2 onions, sliced
1 garlic clove, crushed
3 tbsp balsamic vinegar
½ tsp xylitol

FOR THE DRESSING
2 tbsp dijon mustard
¼ cup extra virgin olive oil
¼ cup white balsamic vinegar
1 tsp chopped fresh thyme leaves
½ tsp xylitol (optional)

1. Preheat the oven to 190°C.
2. Put the kale, lemon juice, salt and oil in a large bowl and massage for 3–4 minutes until it begins to wilt and become soft. Set aside.
3. Place the pumpkin wedges on a baking tray, drizzle with olive oil and season. Roast for 15 minutes, then add the tomatoes and pumpkin seeds and roast for another 15 minutes until the pumpkin is golden and cooked through.
4. Melt the butter in a frying pan. Add the onion and fry for 5 minutes until golden and caramelised. Add the garlic, balsamic vinegar and xylitol and cook for another 5 minutes until caramelised. Remove from the heat and set aside.
5. For the dressing: Whisk all the ingredients together and season to taste.
6. To serve: Arrange kale, roasted veg and onion mixture on a serving platter. Drizzle with dressing and season to taste.

Coronation chicken

Serves 4

KEEP ON TRACK *per serving*

Fat 31g | Carbs 7g | Protein 41g

FOR THE MAYONNAISE
1 large egg yolk
juice of ½ lemon
himalayan salt
½ cup extra virgin olive oil

2 tbsp curry powder
1 tsp xylitol
600g cooked chicken breast, deboned and sliced into chunks
2 tbsp chopped fresh coriander, plus extra to garnish
black pepper

300g broccoli 'rice', to serve

1. For the mayonnaise: Place the egg yolk, lemon juice and a pinch of salt in a bowl.
Whisk together until creamy.
2. Slowly whisk in the oil, about 1 tbsp at a time, until a thick, creamy mayonnaise is formed.
3. Add remaining ingredients, season to taste and toss together well.
4. To serve: Serve the coronation chicken with warm broccoli 'rice'.

nut and dairy free

Deluxe veggie burgers
Serves 6–8

Fat 8g | Carbs 26g | Protein 4g

1 tbsp butter
1 onion, grated or extra finely chopped
4 garlic cloves, crushed
200g button mushrooms, finely chopped
200g courgettes, grated
500g red sweet potatoes, roasted and mashed
2 tbsp psyllium husks
1 tbsp ground coriander
2 tsp ground cumin
½ tsp dried chilli flakes, crushed (optional)
himalayan salt and black pepper, to taste
coconut oil, for frying

TO SERVE
100g wild rocket
100g baby spinach
100g watercress
250g rosa tomatoes, quartered
extra virgin olive oil, for drizzling

1. Melt the butter in a pan and fry the onion until golden, add the garlic and mushrooms and cook until all the excess moisture has evaporated. Transfer the mixture to a large bowl and set aside to cool.
2. Add the remaining ingredients to the onion mixture.
3. Mould the mixture into patties and refrigerate until needed.
4. Heat 1 tbsp coconut oil in a nonstick frying pan and fry patties until golden.
5. To serve: Toss salad leaves and tomato with a little olive oil, salt and pepper and serve veggie burgers hot, topped with the salad.

nut and dairy free

Spicy trout fishcakes with pesto aioli

Makes 12 medium-sized fishcakes

KEEP ON TRACK *per fishcake*

Fat 30g | Carbs 14g | Protein 16g

FOR THE FISHCAKES
600g skinless, boneless trout fillets, cooked
300g sweet potato, cooked and mashed
3 spring onions, finely chopped
4 garlic cloves, crushed
1 tsp each ground cumin and coriander
½ tsp dried chilli flakes, crushed
3 tbsp finely chopped fresh coriander
3 tbsp finely chopped flat-leaf parsley
himalayan salt and black pepper, to taste

FOR THE AIOLI
1 cup homemade mayonnaise (see page 76)
2 tbsp homemade basil pesto

FOR THE COATING
1 cup coconut flour
2 eggs, beaten
2 cups desiccated coconut

1 cup coconut oil, for frying

1. For the fishcakes: Combine all the ingredients in a bowl and season well.
2. Shape the mixture into patties and chill until firm.
3. For the aioli: Combine the ingredients in a serving bowl, season and set aside.
4. For the coating: Dip the fishcakes in coconut flour, then egg and finally desiccated coconut and set aside.
5. Melt the coconut oil in a pan and fry the fishcakes for 1–2 minutes on each side, until golden brown. Drain on paper towel.
6. To serve: Serve the fishcakes warm with the aioli for dipping.

Nut-free, dairy-free brownies

Makes 16 brownies

KEEP ON TRACK *per serving*

Fat 12g | Carbs 12g | Protein 3g

3 cups grated sweet potato
3 large eggs
2 tsp vanilla extract
⅓ cup xylitol
¾ cup melted coconut oil
¾ cup cocoa powder, sifted
2 tsp baking powder
3 tbsp coconut flour
pinch himalayan salt

TO SERVE
cocoa powder
xylitol icing
fresh berries

1. Preheat the oven to 170°C and grease and line a 22cm square baking tin with baking paper.
2. Place the grated sweet potato, eggs, vanilla, xylitol and coconut oil in a large bowl and mix together until well combined.
3. Add the remaining ingredients and mix to form a smooth batter.
4. Pour the mixture into the prepared tin and bake for 30–35 minutes until just set to the touch. Allow the brownies to cool in the tin.
5. To serve: Cut the brownies into squares and serve dusted with cocoa powder and xylitol icing, and garnished with fresh berries.

Sweet treats

LISA THOMAS

Pilates teacher and mother

Lisa started eating LCHF in 2010 when she fell pregnant. ('I simply started to crave fatty food. And this was way before any pro-fat conversations had reached the mainstream,' she says.) As a classical ballerina, Lisa had never eaten that way before, but she went with it 'because I felt my body knew best'. After a healthy, happy pregnancy and successfully breastfeeding Logan for 10 months, Lisa started radiation therapy for a desmoid tumour which, while not malignant, was nonetheless locally aggressive. 'In researching my tumour, I found that there are so many links between cancer and sugar that even my doctor advocated that I continue to eat this way,' she says, and she attributes getting through the treatment as well as she did to her diet. Since then, the entire Thomas family – Lisa, her husband Craig and Logan, their six-year-old son, have all followed a low-carb diet.

'The research I've done myself around the effect of sugar on children makes cutting it out of their diets a no-brainer. Eating LCHF is our normal for our family, but it doesn't come without judgement from other parents!

'My two pet peeves are, firstly, the perception that my child is being deprived – I mean, when did childhood become about eating rubbish? And, secondly, that I slave away in the kitchen all day preparing weird food. If you think about it, our grandparents didn't have all this sugary fast food that we are so-called depriving our child of today. And when you get the hang of eating low carb, it takes no more time than any other meal to prepare.

'And you can be really creative! Logan has had some of the best birthday parties you can imagine. He doesn't have a taste for sugar, so he doesn't need a replacement sweetener. Sometimes he has a touch of honey, but that's all.

'For me, eating low carb as a family is about shifting the paradigm. It's not about restricting food – it's about normalising the way we eat. I am really passionate about children eating healthily – Logan eats anything: liver, olives, you name it. There is no special fuss because he's a child, no bribing him to eat vegetables. He just loves it all.

'This is our normal.'

http://lisathomasstudio.com

Lisa's sweet potato cupcakes

Makes 12 cupcakes or 2 x 20cm cakes

Fat 21g | Carbs 18g | Protein 6g

FOR THE CAKE MIX
1½ cups sweet potato, cooked and mashed
4 eggs
4 tbsp coconut oil
5 tbsp coconut flour
⅔ cup cocoa powder
50ml honey
3 tsp baking powder
½ tsp salt
70g walnuts or pecan nuts, chopped

FOR THE ICING
250g full cream mascarpone
1–2 tsp honey
2 tbsp cocoa powder

1. For the cake mix: Preheat the oven to 180°C. Place cupcake liners in a 12-hole muffin tin or grease and line 2 × 20cm cake tins with baking paper.
2. Place all the cake ingredients, except the nuts, in a food processor and blitz together. Transfer the mixture to a bowl, and stir in the chopped nuts.
3. Spoon the mixture into the paper cases and bake for 20 minutes, or until the mixture is cooked through. Remove and allow to cool completely before icing.
4. For the icing: Mix all the ingredients together by hand, taking care not to overmix, as the icing may become runny. Decorate with nuts and grated 99% dark chocolate, if desired.

Note: If you need nut-free cupcakes, the nuts can be left out.

If you have really nice sweet potatoes, you need much less honey.

Chocolate frozen dessert

Serves 6

Fat 18g | Carbs 1g | Protein 3g

2 eggs, separated
1 tbsp cocoa powder
1 cup cream
80g xylitol

pomegranate rubies, to garnish
cocoa powder, to dust

1. Place the egg yolks in a bowl and whisk until creamy and smooth. Dissolve the cocoa in ½ cup water, add to the yolks and stir to combine.
2. Place the cream and xylitol in a bowl and whip until stiff.
3. Place the egg whites in a bowl and whip until stiff. Stir the cream into the yolk mixture, then fold in the egg white.
4. Pour into small moulds. Freeze for 4 hours or overnight to set.
5. To serve: Unmould onto a serving plate. Garnish with pomegranate rubies and dust with cocoa powder.

Yoghurt rose panna cotta with a berry jelly

Serves 6

per serving

Fat 6g | Carbs 9g | Protein 7g

FOR THE BERRY JELLY
½ cup water
2 tbsp xylitol
2 tsp rose water
1 tbsp powdered gelatine, sprinkled over 3 tbsp water
150g raspberries
100g pomegranate rubies

FOR THE PANNA COTTA
½ cup water
50g xylitol
1 tsp rose water
1 vanilla pod, halved and seeds scraped out
1½ tbsp powdered gelatine
2½ cups double cream yoghurt

1. For the berry jelly: Place the water, xylitol and rose water in a small saucepan and stir over a medium heat until xylitol has dissolved. Remove from the heat, add soaked gelatine and stir until dissolved. Cool slightly.
2. Divide the berries and pomegranate rubies between 6 lightly oiled 200ml moulds. Cover the berries with the gelatine mixture, place in the fridge and allow to set.
3. For the panna cotta: Place the water, xylitol, rose water and vanilla seeds in a small saucepan and stir until the xylitol has dissolved. Add the gelatine and stir until completely dissolved. Cool slightly. Whisk in the yoghurt, ensuring that it is thoroughly combined. Pour the mixture over the set berry jellies and tap lightly on a board to ensure there are no air pockets. Cover and refrigerate for at least 4 hours, or until set.
4. To serve: Invert the panna cottas onto serving plates and serve immediately.

Courgette cake

Serves 10

Fat 24g | Carbs 2g | Protein 6g

2 eggs, separated
½ cup extra virgin olive oil
80g xylitol
grated zest of ½ lemon
1 cup grated courgette
200g ground almonds
1 tsp baking powder
1 tsp allspice

xylitol syrup, to drizzle (optional)

1. Preheat the oven to 160°C. Grease a 17cm bundt tin.
2. Place the egg yolks and olive oil in a bowl and whisk until
pale and creamy.
3. Whisk the egg whites in a separate bowl until stiff peaks form.
Set aside.
4. Combine the egg yolk mixture with the remaining ingredients,
folding in the egg white at the very end. Pour into the prepared tin
and bake for 40 minutes.
5. Allow to cool in the tin, then invert the cake onto a rack to cool
completely.
6. To serve: Drizzle with a little xylitol syrup, if desired, and serve
with a cup of black tea or coffee with cream.

Deluxe chocolate fudge truffles

Makes 20

KEEP ON TRACK *per serving*

Fat 6g | **Carbs 2g** | **Protein 1g**

3 tbsp coconut oil
¼ cup cream
50g 85% dark chocolate
3 tbsp xylitol
3 tbsp cocoa powder
100g cream cheese
pinch himalayan salt

extra cocoa powder, to coat truffles

1. Line a 21cm square baking tin with foil.
2. Place coconut oil, cream, dark chocolate, xylitol and cocoa powder in a saucepan. Stir over a medium heat until chocolate is melted and mixture is smooth.
3. Remove from the heat and leave mixture to cool slightly.
4. Whisk cream cheese and salt into the warm chocolate mixture until well combined and pour into the prepared tin. Refrigerate for 2–3 hours or until set.
5. Shape spoonfuls of the set mixture into balls and roll in extra cocoa powder to make truffles.
6. If making in advance, truffles can be stored in an airtight container in the fridge for 1 week.

Yoghurt orange tart

Serves 8

KEEP ON TRACK *per serving*

Fat 26g | Carbs 14g | Protein 10g

FOR THE CRUST
100g desiccated coconut
100g sesame seeds
2 tbsp cocoa powder
¼ cup melted coconut oil

FOR THE FILLING
400g double cream yoghurt, at room temperature
80g xylitol
2 whole eggs
2 egg yolks
grated zest of 1 orange
1 tsp orange blossom water

blueberries, to garnish

1. For the crust: Preheat the oven to 180°C. Place the coconut, sesame seeds and cocoa powder in a blender and pulse until well combined. Add the coconut oil and pulse again until all the ingredients are 'wet'.
2. Press into a 20cm long loose-based tart tin and bake in the oven for 10 minutes. Remove and allow to cool.
3. Reduce the oven temperature to 160°C.
4. For the filling: Place the yoghurt in a large bowl, beat in the xylitol and add the eggs and egg yolks, one at a time, whisking well after each addition. Stir in the orange zest and orange blossom water.
5. Pour the mixture into the base and bake for 30–40 minutes or until firm but still slightly wobbly in the centre. Allow to cool in the oven.
6. Remove and cool completely, then refrigerate for at least 4 hours, or preferably overnight.
7. To serve: Serve the tart sliced and topped with blueberries.

Pistachio and saffron-style kulfi

Serves 4

KEEP ON TRACK *per serving*

Fat 36g | Carbs 6g | Protein 6g

3 tbsp xylitol
1 egg
1 egg yolk
2 cups cream
6 cardamom pods, bruised
big pinch of saffron in a little hot water
50g pistachio nuts, chopped

1. Place the xylitol, egg and egg yolk in a bowl and whisk until pale and fluffy. Set aside.
2. Place 1 cup cream in a pot along with the cardamom pods and saffron. Bring to just below a boil, remove from heat, allow to cool slightly, then strain into a jug.
3. Add the warm cream to the egg mixture, whisking constantly, then return this mixture to the pot and warm over a very low heat, stirring until thickened. Remove from the heat and set aside to cool.
4. Place the remaining 1 cup cream in a bowl and whisk until firm, then fold into the cooled custard. Pour mixture into 80ml moulds and freeze until firm.
5. To serve: Unmould kulfis and scatter with nuts.

Christmas cassata

Serves 8

KEEP ON TRACK *per serving*

Fat 22g | Carbs 19g | Protein 11g

2kg double cream yoghurt
70g xylitol
100g raspberries, blitzed until smooth
2 tbsp cocoa powder, dissolved in a little warm water

60g 80% dark chocolate, melted, to drizzle
pomegranate rubies, to garnish
pistachio nuts, to garnish

1. Place the yoghurt in a bowl with the xylitol and beat until smooth and well combined.
2. Divide the mixture evenly between 3 bowls, then stir the blitzed raspberries into the first bowl of yoghurt until completely combined, stir the cocoa powder into the second bowl of yoghurt, and leave the third bowl plain.
3. Oil a 2ℓ mould. Alternate pouring a little of each mixture into the mould to form layers and continue until all three mixtures have been used up, and a marble effect has been created.
4. Freeze the mould overnight.
5. To serve: Dip the mould into a bowl of warm water and unmould it onto a serving platter. Drizzle with the chocolate and garnish with pomegranate rubies and nuts.

Lemon meringue pie

Serves 10

KEEP ON TRACK *per serving*

Fat 18g | Carbs 4g | Protein 5g

FOR THE BASE
50g almonds
50g pecan nuts
100g desiccated coconut
pinch himalayan salt
2 tsp raw cacao
40g butter, melted

FOR THE LEMON CURD
½ cup freshly squeezed lemon juice
2 tsp finely grated lemon zest
50g xylitol
3 whole large eggs
50g butter, cubed

FOR THE MERINGUE
3 egg whites
40g xylitol

1. Preheat the oven to 180°C. Place the nuts and coconut onto a baking tray and bake for 20 minutes or until golden. Cool slightly.
2. For the base: Pulse the nuts, coconut, salt and cacao in a blender until fine but not oily. Stir in the butter. Press mixture into a 20cm-diameter pie dish and bake for about 20 minutes or until golden. Set aside. Reduce oven temperature to 160°C.
3. For the lemon curd: Place all the ingredients, except the butter, in a glass bowl and whisk over a bain-marie until the xylitol dissolves. Now add the butter – a few blocks at a time – continuing to whisk until incorporated. Cook the curd until it thickens, then pour it over the base and set aside.
4. For the meringue: Whisk the egg whites to stiff peak stage and slowly whisk in the xylitol a little at a time until the meringue is thick and glossy. Pile the meringue on top of the curd and bake for 35–40 minutes, or until pale golden and set.
5. Allow to cool completely before serving, preferably overnight.
6. To serve: Slice the pie and serve with a cup of black tea or coffee with cream.

ACKNOWLEDGEMENTS

Thank you to all the LOSE IT! readers who insisted we compile our recipes – we had a lot of fun putting this book together! And thank you, all of you, for constantly inspiring us with stories of your success – in particular those who've shared your stories (and favourite recipes) here. It's a constant reward and privilege to be part of your process.

INDEX

A

aioli, pesto 178–179
anchovy and courgette fritters, with basil cream sauce 34–35
apple salad 136–137
Asian-style salmon and cucumber salad 70–71
aubergines, *see* eggplants

B

balsamic
   onions 122–123
   pork neck braise 142–143
   salad 98–99
bars, coconut, goji berry and macadamia 164–165
basic rules 8–12
basil cream sauce 34–35
beef
   and balsamic salad 98–99
   bolognaise with zoodles 94–95
   braciole 90–91
   brisket, Brian's 88–89
   chilli con carne with crispy eggplant 96–97
   eggplant rolls in creamy tomato sauce 102–103
   Italian-style short ribs 108–109
   peppered fillet with salsa verde 100–101
   pot roast with mushroom gravy 106–107
   rump steak with parmesan fried mushrooms 92–93
   Thai salad 104–105
Berkman, Brian 86–89
bolognaise, beef 94–95
braciole, beef 90–91
brisket, Brian's 88–89
broccoli and cauliflower falafels 26–27
brownies, nut-free, dairy-free 180–181
burgers, deluxe veggie 176–177
butter, lemon peri-peri 46–47
buttermilk chive dressing 50–51

C

cake, courgette 192–193
caprese-stuffed tomatoes, roasted 160–161
cassata, Christmas 200–201
casserole, Italian-style lamb 116–117
Catalan tomato fish with saffron mayonnaise 76–77
cauliflower
   and broccoli falafels 26–27
   cumin-roasted 78–79
   spicy salad 28–29
cauli pizza, *see* pizzas

chicken
   coconut curry, Hennie's 44–45
   coconut curry, spicy 54–55
   coronation 174–175
   grilled, and rocket pesto zoodles 58–59
   paprika, with buttermilk chive dressing 50–51
   rolled stuffed breasts 52–53
   salad with mint dressing 48–49
   spatchcock, with lemon peri-peri butter 46–47
   yoghurt-marinated, with coriander sauce 56–57
chilli con carne, beef 96–97
chocolate
   frozen dessert 188–189
   truffles 194–195
Christmas cassata 200–201
coconut
   chicken curry, Hennie's 44–45
   chicken curry, spicy 54–55
   goji berry and macadamia bars 164–165
Coetzee, Hennie 42–45
coriander sauce 56–57
coronation chicken 174–175
courgettes
   and anchovy fritters 34–35
   cake 192–193
   fries 68–69
   'noodles', stir-fry with 144–145
   zoodles 94–95
crackers, poppy seed 158–159
cucumber salad 70–71
cumin-roasted cauliflower with prawns 78–79
cupcakes, Lisa's sweet potato 186–187
curry
   coconut chicken, Hennie's 44–45
   coconut chicken, spicy 54–55
   lamb, Reyhana's 170–171

D

dairy free, *see* nut and dairy free
dips
   Moutabel-style eggplant 24–25
   red pepper and walnut 124–125

E

eggplants
   crispy 96–97
   and lamb bakes 120–121
   mini pizzas 32–33
   Moutabel-style dip 24–25
   rolls in creamy tomato sauce 102–103

eggs
    green omelette, Shannon's 154–155
    scotch 162–163
    smoked salmon eggs Benedict 156–157

F
falafels, broccoli and cauliflower 26–27
frittata, smoked salmon, leek, dill and cream
    cheese 160–161
fritters, anchovy and courgette 34–35

G
gammon with raspberry glaze 134–135
garlic ginger and coconut prawns, Nicky's
    64–65
goat's cheese, baked mushrooms and 22–23
goji berry, coconut and macadamia bars
    164–165

H
hake
    Catalan tomato fish 76–77
    crumbed 68–69
harissa lamb kebabs with balsamic onions
    122–123

I
Italian-style
    beef short ribs 108–109
    lamb casserole 116–117

K
kale, caramelised onion, roasted pumpkin and
    vine tomato salad 172–173
kebabs, harissa lamb 122–123
Kiggen, Justine 18–19
kulfi, pistachio and saffron-style 198–199

L
lamb
    curry, Reyhana's 170–171
    and eggplant bakes 120–121
    harissa kebabs with balsamic onions
        122–123
    Italian-style casserole 116–117
    loin chops with red pepper and walnut dip
        124–125
    patties on banting wraps 126–127
    shanks in rich tomato sauce 118–119
    Sunday lunch leg of 114–115
    tagine of shanks 112–113
lemon meringue pie 202–203
lemon peri-peri butter 46–47

M
mayonnaise, saffron 76–77
McLaughlin, Shannon 152–155
mint dressing 48–49

Moutabel-style eggplant dip 24–25
mushrooms
    and goat's cheese 22–23
    gravy 106–107
    parmesan fried 92–93
    pâté 158–159

N
nut and dairy free
    brownies 180–181
    coronation chicken 174–175
    deluxe veggie burgers 176–177
    kale, caramelised onion, roasted pumpkin
        and vine tomato salad 172–173
    lamb curry, Reyhana's 170–171
    trout fishcakes with pesto aioli 178–179

O
omelette, Shannon's green 154–155
onions, balsamic 122–123

P
pancetta, pork sausages with 138–139
panna cotta, yoghurt rose 190–191
paprika
    chicken with buttermilk chive dressing
        50–51
    pork fillet with apple salad 136–137
pâté, mushroom 158–159
peppered fillet with salsa verde 100–101
peri-peri butter 46–47
Perks, Nicky 62–65
pesto
    aioli 178–179
    rocket 58–59
    watercress 66–67
pistachio and saffron-style kulfi 198–199
pizzas
    base 73
    with crème fraîche and smoked salmon
        72–73
    mini eggplant 32–33
    with roast garlic and shredded pork 146–147
    with tomato, blue cheese and walnut 20–21
poppy seed crackers 158–159
pork
    balsamic neck braise 142–143
    gammon with raspberry glaze 134–135
    loin stir-fry, Sharon's 132–133
    pizzas with roast garlic and shredded
        146–147
    roast belly with crispy crackling 140–141
    sausages with pancetta 138–139
    scotch eggs 162–163
    spinach and feta-filled chops 148–149
    and tomato stir-fry 144–145
    warm paprika fillet with apple salad 136–137
pot roast, beef 106–107

prawns
  cumin-roasted cauliflower with 78–79
  garlic ginger and coconut, Nicky's 64–65
  and tomato salad 80–81

R
raspberry glaze, gammon with 134–135
red pepper and walnut dip 124–125
rocket
  pesto zoodles 58–59
  salsa verde 100–101
röstis 156–157
rump steak with parmesan fried mushrooms 92–93

S
saffron mayonnaise 76–77
sage, onion and pork scotch eggs 162–163
salad dressings
  buttermilk chive 50–51
  mint 48–49
  tomato 80–81
salads
  apple 136–137
  balsamic 98–99
  chicken, with mint dressing 48–49
  cucumber 70–71
  kale, caramelised onion, roasted pumpkin
    and vine tomato 172–173
  spicy cauliflower 28–29
  Thai beef 104–105
  tomato prawn 80–81
salmon
  Asian-style 70–71
  and cream cheese terrine 74–75
  and eggs Benedict 156–157
  frittata 160–161
  pizza with crème fraîche and 72–73
salsa verde 100–101
scotch eggs 162–163
snoek with fresh tomato salad and watercress
  pesto 66–67
spatchcock chicken with lemon peri-peri butter
  46–47
spinach and feta-filled pork chops 148–149
stir-fry
  pork loin, Sharon's 132–133
  tomato and pork 144–145
Sunday lunch leg of lamb 114–115
sweet potato cupcakes, Lisa's 186–187
sweet treats
  chocolate frozen dessert 188–189
  Christmas cassata 200–201
  coconut, goji berry and macadamia bars
    164–165
  courgette cake 192–193
  deluxe chocolate fudge truffles 194–195
  lemon meringue pie 202–203

nut-free, dairy-free brownies 180–181
pistachio and saffron-style kulfi 198–199
sweet potato cupcakes, Lisa's 186–187
yoghurt orange tart 196–197
yoghurt rose panna cotta with berry jelly
  190–191

T
tagine of lamb shanks 112–113
terrine, smoked salmon and cream cheese
  74–75
Thai beef salad 104–105
Thomas, Lisa 184–187
Thumbran, Reyhana 168–171
tomatoes
  dressing 80–81
  roasted caprese-stuffed 160–161
trout fishcakes with pesto aioli 178–179
truffles, deluxe chocolate fudge 194–195

V
Van Wyk, Sharon 130–133
vegetable bake, winter 36–37
vegetarian
  anchovy and courgette fritters 34–35
  baked mushrooms and goat's cheese 22–23
  broccoli and cauliflower falafels 26–27
  cauli pizza with tomato, blue cheese and
    walnut 20–21
  deluxe veggie burgers 176–177
  mini eggplant pizzas 32–33
  Moutabel-style eggplant dip 24–25
  spicy cauliflower salad with poached egg
    28–29
  winter vegetable bake 36–37
veggie burgers, deluxe 176–177

W
watercress pesto 66–67
wraps, lamb patties on banting 126–127

Y
yoghurt
  -marinated chicken 56–57
  orange tart 196–197
  rose panna cotta with berry jelly 190–191

Z
zucchini, *see* courgettes

SUNBIRD PUBLISHERS

Text © *LOSE IT!* magazine 2016
Published edition © 2016 Sunbird Publishers

Originally published in South Africa in 2016 by Sunbird Publishers
The illustrated imprint of Jonathan Ball Publishers
A division of Media24 (Pty) Ltd
PO Box 33977
Jeppestown
2043

Twitter: www.twitter.com/JonathanBallPub
Facebook: www.facebook.com/JonathanBallPublishers
Blog: http://jonathanball.bookslive.co.za/

www.loseit.co.za

ISBN 978 1 86842 768 0

*Every effort has been made to trace the copyright holders and to obtain their permission for the
use of copyright material. The publishers apologise for any errors or omissions and would be
grateful to be notified of any corrections that should be incorporated in future editions of this book.*

Food stylist: Justine Kiggen
Styling assistant: Pia-Alexa Duarte
Photographs by Dawie Verwey, Donna Lewis, Jo Spies, Anèl van der Merwe, Liza van Deventer,
Meliza Myburgh, Thinkstock
Printed and bound by CTP Printers, Cape Town
Set in Helvetica Neue LT Std, Serifa Std, Wendy LP Std

LOSE IT! magazine is published by Media24 (Pty) Ltd, Naspers Centre, 40 Heerengracht,
Cape Town, 8001. The content is not intended to substitute medical advice from a qualified
healthcare professional.